Britannic Myths

Britannic Myths

by

Steven O'Brien

Paintings by Joe Machine

Holland House Books

Paperback ISBN: 978-1-910688-50-2

Printed and bound in Great Britain by
Intype Libra Ltd., London

Typeset and design by Lucy Binnersley

Published in the UK
Holland House Books
Holland House
47 Greenham Road
Newbury, Berkshire RG14 7HY
United Kingdom

www.hhousebooks.com

To Eric and Terry for the love, laughter and stories, and
Christian Sweeting for his generosity.
- Steven O'Brien

For my dear friend Charles Thomson, with thanks for your
friendship, support and guidance over the years.
- Joe Machine

Contents

Introduction   i

The Leprechaun   1

Child Roland   11

Herne   27

St Dunstan and the Devil   39

Wayland   51

The White Stag   59

The Selkie   67

Tuatha Dé Danann   87

Cú Chulainn and the Morrigan   95

O'Carolan   125

Peggy Colligan and the Bucket   129

The Lennan Sidh   135

The Headless Coachman   147

The Changeling   151

Math Son of Mathonwy   167

Arianrhod   175

Blodeuedd   189

Painting the Myth by Joe Machine   207

Introduction

I find it strange that the people of these islands often know more about the pantheons of Greece and Rome than they do of the mythic hoard of our own lands. The sandals, lyres and olive groves of the south seem to pull the imagination away from our cool mists and deep greens. Sitting under a cypress, overlooking the ink-blue Aegean might put one in mind of Hermes, satyrs and the cyclops, but I would much rather go into an oak wood and listen for whispers. For me it began with my grandfather's telling of the Leprechaun – but more of that spiky little fellow later.

The French have made a great celebration of the pedigree of their food and wine. They assert that the essences of the earth have a bearing on the specificity and quality of its produce. Well, the stories and illustrations in this book are part of our own terroir, to borrow the French term. The characters who thrive in these narratives spring straight form our own landscape. They are of the rocks, the scrubby pastures and the coming rain. Peeling away the topsoil of these tales is a tricky business (if, that is, we concern ourselves with origins). Yet turning place names and half remembered historical figures over on our tongues allows for a savouring of the complex interactions and exchanges which have produced the mythic and folkloric matter of this place.

Highdown Hill is not far from where I live in Sussex. They say the Saxon king Ælle is buried there and fierce, rusty angon spears have been dug from the chalk, telling us that the very first English invaders believed the place to be sacred. Chichester, the old Roman city of Noviomagus Reginorum was renamed in honour of Ælle's son Cissa. He also gave his name to the great hillfort of Cissbury Ring, which lies about two miles from my house. Yet we know that both Highdown and Cissbury were delved and shaped by people long before the English came. Most of the people who lived in Noviomagus Reginorum were Romanised natives that we call Celts. They would have used Latin for commerce and education, and their own language for love, home, and hearthside stories. That language was Brythonic, the ancestor of the Welsh language, once spoken from the tip of Cornwall to the mountains of Scotland (not that either place was named as such back then). Its sister tongue, Goidelic, or Old Irish was spoken across the sea, to the west.

Of course it is ultimately futile to look for a single original source to these stories. They have been told and told again a million times. They have accrued much narrative baggage. Picts, Britons, Scots, Gaels, Saxons, and Normans have all sat around the 'pot of generation' and seasoned the stew. Indeed, many of the stories included here have even wider echoes; Cú Chulainn, the great Irish hero is similar in his rages and battle feats to the muscle-girt Heracles. More surprisingly, Cú Chulainn's story chimes the Persian hero Rostem, who also slew his own son in combat. The vengeful and seductive Morrigan could almost be an unpredictable deity of the Hindu pantheon. Herne, as Lord of Beasts, features in kindred tales all across Eurasia and beyond. Perhaps these stories show that there was once a corpus of sacred narratives common to all the ancient Indo European tribes. Perhaps the stories demonstrate in a Jungian fashion, that we are merely hardwired to tell similar stories, populated with similar characters all over the world, and in all times. Perhaps the ancestors of these stories were told around flickering campfires in cave mouths by our distant shaggy ancestors warming themselves against the withering cold the last ice age.

What is certain is that there must have been a great sharing of these stories all across the islands; the Irish sea god Manannán mac Lir crops up in medieval Welsh literature as Manawydan fab Llyr. There are tales of King Arthur from Scotland and Ireland. Wayland the Smith, as English as his stone chamber in the southern downlands, seems the almost to be the brother of Culann the Smith of the Ulster Cycle. I think the very sea-hemmed geography of these islands has resulted in a particular blending and percolation.

This book then is a celebration of stories and of storytelling, and also of their layers. For instance, let me go back to the figure of King Arthur. It will shock some to be told that Arthur was never a king and neither, for that matter, was he English. Imagine a warm spring day in the 500s. The Saxons have come. They are winning skirmish after skirmish. Think of an officer in the army of the Britons. He is dressed as a Roman aristocrat. He looks around at his cavalrymen stirring in the dawn, fitting bridles to their horses. His name is Artorious and he is Dux Bellorum, or Duke of Battles. He has been in Gaul and once as far as Ravenna. The legions have long gone, but this scarred and tenacious man, this Artorius, and others like him have made a name for themselves in marshalling the resistance to the fair- haired foreign warriors who have sailed in from across the North Sea. He is determined to protect what is left of the ordered life of villas, vineyards and baths.

The cavalryman Artorius will go down in glory and defeat. The English will occupy much of the land and name it for themselves. The Welsh will keep the memory of this Artorius alive in their poems and songs. Later on, monks like Gildas and Nennius and William of Malmesbury will quarrel down through the centuries about this man of whom many stories are told. They will wonder where Camlann is, site of the fatal battle where Arthur perished. They will contradict each other about his kingship and his prowess. The English will tell stories of Arthur and so will the Irish and Scots. When the Normans come they discover Arthur and they take him to their hearts. They invest him with the first inklings of chivalry and also with high medieval

Christianity. Later generations make him into an armour-plated, wise monarch, wedded to a beautiful queen. He lives in a many towered castle and keeps company with questing knights.

Now I began with Arthur the Romano-Celtic cavalry officer. I have finished with the bearded and sagacious king. Yet there are aspects of Arthur which must predate even the twilight of Roman life in Britain. In the Mabinogion we are given stories of Arthur chasing a giant boar through an enchanted forest. There is feasting and a great mysterious cauldron. Look closer at the key names and older ideas are revealed; Guinevere - through Welsh Gwenhyfar, and then from Irish Findabair means 'the white spirit.' Lancelot Du Lac, perhaps began as the Irish god Lugh Lonbemnech. Certainly Lancelot comes from the waters of a lake (Du Lac), one of the classic marches where our reality touches that of the Celtic otherworld. So even in the full flowering of his majesty, Arthur is surrounded by attendant players who have veneers of the medieval but the cores of ancient pre-Christian figures. The name Arthur itself is often taken to derive from the old Brythonic Arto-rig, or 'Bear King.' To come close to Arthur we need to look at him in all his incarnations, but we may feel a tingle when we see something very old indeed in him.

I owe a great deal to the other writers in this slipstream. Lady Gregory, Eileen O'Faoláin Robert Graves, Jaqueline Simpson, WB Yeats, Marina Warner and Ian Mackay have all been pathfinders. But it was my grandfather, with his ghosts and banshees and the Leprechaun who first showed me that these stories are a kind of birth-right. I have long wished to devote time to retelling some of the tales and the collaboration with Joe Machine brought both boundaries and possibilities. The collection is partial and selective. Given more time there might have been more of them, but we worked on those that whispered loudest to us at the time.

We decided to call it 'Britannic Myths' after much discussion, although we both know that some of the material is folkloric, and not myth in the strictest sense of the word. You might have noticed that I refer several times to 'these islands'. This is because the stories have been taken from right across the British Isles, which is strictly a geographical, yet contentious term, since many people in the Republic of Ireland would be loath to sit comfortably within such a definition. Joe and I turned to Seamus Heaney for inspiration (poets will always give you sideways but useful advice). In his essay 'Through-Other Places, Through Other Times' Heaney writes of the term 'Britannic':

> 'there is a wonderful originality, in all senses, about employing instead the word 'Britannic,' Britannic works more like a cultural wake-up call and gestures not only towards the cultural past but also towards an imaginable future.'

For me, 'Britannic' has a certain Celtic/Saxon alloy to it, and the term creates a space to take in the stories of the four nations of these islands. As mythographers, Joe and I are merely attempting to re-utter some of the stories and pass them on in a fresh fashion.

Working with Joe has been a shared journey into the cultural past. Joe understands the primal and pared bones of these stories. He has a great knack for portraying the strange violence, eroticism and magic. The process of our collaboration began with me giving Joe the retellings as I finished them. He then painted them. However, it soon grew into a more twining exploration. At times Joe would only ask me for the bare outline of the story, then he would send the paintings to me and I fleshed the narrative in response. Occasionally Joe asked merely for titles and I would tell the story of the subsequent painting. I hope he will agree with me that our collaboration has led us deeper into the stories than we first envisaged. When I look at his paintings I am struck mostly by the muscular life of them. He re-conjures tales so that the viewer can believe in them anew. To use an old Scots word, it is a wanchancy experience to stand before Joe's paintings such as The Devil and St Dunstan and The Death of Cú Chulainn. They shiver with ancient magic. It has been a great pleasure to walk with him into the forest of whispers. Where it all began with the Leprechaun.

The Leprechaun

*A*nd so it all began with my grandad and the Leprechaun. He was a great man for singing and stories. His generation were happy to turn the television off on a Sunday evening and fill the silence with word-conjure.

As I look back now, I see him in his mustard cardigan and suede shoes. His dentures gleam and his hair is Brylcreemed back, as slick as an otter's pelt. The false teeth give his speech a whistling quality now and then. When he tells stories he often runs an open palm over his oily hair. I am eleven years old and he is not much taller than me. Spare and dapper; when he sings he stands by the fireplace with one hand behind his back. There is a bantam dignity about him.

He loves to scare us. Sometimes he puts one of my grandmother's shawls over his head and rises from behind the sofa as the very likeness of the banshee. My brother, my sister and I laugh in a scared-ticklish way. Such is the theatricality of his moaning and hunching over us that we never really believe his banshee story. But with the story of the Leprechaun it was different. He will tell us about his encounter with the little man in a matter of fact way, in much the same tone as when he recounts his reminiscences of his own raw and half-starved childhood, or when he used to hunt plovers for the gentry. So although I am eleven years old, I am only just beginning to question the veracity of the story. It certainly has no less a ring of truth to it than his claim to have cycled sixty miles there and back in one night just to go to a party.

Imagine you take a picture of us with a 1970's Polaroid camera.

The gaudy orange and yellows of the instant photo shows an ordinary family in a neat small house. My father and mother are smoking and sipping their third cup of tea. My grandmother is ironing. We three children are on the sofa. Grandad is in his armchair.

He keeps himself busy doing a bit of painting and decorating and he always wears a collar and tie under his overalls. The talk passes through Mrs Knight's new bathroom which he finished last week, to the next job at the doctor's house. My father mentions the sunset the night before, when he and I were walking our dog Jasper along the beach. Grandad has that Irish way of quietly agreeing by giving a soft intake of breath, like a sigh in reverse. My father stops speaking and there is silence. There are dark corners in the sitting room.

Grandad looks around and says, 'It puts me in mind of the evening I met the Leprechaun.' And to the hiss and sweep of my grandmother's steam iron he begins to lay before us the tale of his encounter.

'When I was a young man I was coming home one late afternoon in April. It had rained but had I been working all day in a barn, cutting turnips. I remember that the rain had just passed and the fields were all washed new. I climbed over a wall to take the short cut home. The grass wet my boots, especially the one with a hole in the sole. I crossed the field and had to skirt a little wood. It was not far from Kildangan. I could see the smoke coming from our chimney. I was just passing by the trees when I noticed a movement. In those days we always carried our jackets over our shoulders if we could, to be ready to throw it over any stray pheasants. You had to be quick and careful. We needed the meat but the law was against us in that matter; you could get prison for poaching. Anyway, I pricked up and looked again to where I had noticed something moving. Well, the sight of it nearly had me running the other way. I felt like rubbing my eyes to see if they were cheating me. For there, by the bank of an old ash tree, squirming and muttering was a little man lying on the ground.

I went up to him with my heart knocking on my ribs. Yes, he was a little man right enough, about the size of a five year old child and he was dressed in a frayed green coat. He had a crumpled, wrinkled face and he was wearing a tall battered hat. As I came close I could hear him cursing and, oh, the swearing and blasphemies. It would make a sailor blush. I suppose the length of my shadow gave me away for he looked up in the midst of his carrying on. He flinched, but then straightaway he seemed to change his demeanour. 'Well hello Martin O'Brien,' he said in a little voice that sounded something like a door hinge creaking.

'Hello yourself,' I replied.

'You find me in a sorry situation altogether Martin,' he said.

'Oh is that so?'

'Yes, terrible,' he said. 'I was just on my way to see my people and this happened.' The little man pointed to his foot. I saw that he had got it stuck under the one of the roots of the ash tree. 'Now how would it be if you could give me a bit of assistance Martin? For I want to be half way to Wicklow by midnight.'

'Wicklow is very long way from here,' I said.

The little man's hazel eyes flashed with annoyance. 'I walk very fast' he said.

'Do you now?' I said, quiet like, as if I wasn't the least bit interested. For the notion had come upon me that the fellow was none other than the Leprechaun and I wanted to think about a plan of action. You have to be very careful when you deal with the 'good people.' Get yourself prepared and be as polite as you can. I drew even closer and had another long look at him. He was like a cross between a tramp and fox. He smelled of the damp woods.

'Yes Martin.' He took off his old hat and bashed it back into shape. His hair was rusty and long. 'I go like the wind and I am running messages all over the country.'

'Well then, let me see,' I said, as I knelt down. I ran my hand the length of the root. It was a thick one. However, I was strong in those days and, closing my fingers around it, I gave it a great wrench. Now, what occurred next, happened in an instant. I was strong but I was also quick and I knew I had to be on this occasion. As I pulled the root up the Leprechaun gave a great yelp of relief, but this soon turned to a wail, for I had caught him, in mid-leap, by his left ear.

How he pulled and screeched. One second he was furious, the next he was in despair, then back to fury again. His language was awful. His little hands pawed at my fingers but I had him fast. 'Now, now Sir,' I said, remembering my manners. 'I have done you a great favour and soon you will be on your way to the Wicklow mountains. But doesn't one favour deserve another in return?'

The Leprechaun brightened up, 'Now that you come to mention it Martin' he said, still straining against my grasp, 'I suppose it does, but If you just let go now I will be able to do something for you the next time I am in Kildangan. Perhaps a bottle of fine whisky?'

'No, no, no,' I replied, giving his ear another little twist. 'That won't do at all and if I let you go I will never see you again.'

'That's an atrocious calumny Martin,' he said. 'I'll have you know that I am of the quality and I always keep my word.'

'Well this is going to be the way of it Sir,' I said. 'I know all about you and your people. I know what a trickster you are. I only want one thing in return for the grand rescue of your good self.'

The Leprechaun stood up as best he could. He held his hat by his side. He looked at me. 'You have me bettered,' he said. 'What can I do for you?'

'Let me see.' I put on my most casual voice. 'I was just thinking that you must have been attending some business in this town-land. So my mind is going along these lines . . . if you just show me where your gold is buried I will let you go.'

'Aw, not that! Not that!' He wailed, and it was like the grief of a cat at midnight.

'Yes, that exactly sir.'

'You'll have me ruined,' he cried.

'Not at all' I replied. You have plenty of treasure all over the place.'

'I never had you down for such a Rapparee, Martin O'Brien!' His tawny eyes filled with tears of rage.

'Enough, enough,' I said. 'You have been gathering gold for a long, long time and I only want the stash you have buried here. Now take me to it. I won't let you go until you do.'

He gave one last wail and then became quiet. 'Alright, alright' he said, taking up a little twisted blackthorn stick. 'This way.'

He led out into the field and then through a gate into a pasture where an old donkey was grazing. All the time I had him by the ear and all the time he was grumbling at the injustice of it all. Several times he looked up at me sideways and several times I nearly tripped over molehills that seemed to spring suddenly up from the grass. But I was ready for these antics. He was just trying to shake me off.

Finally he turned us both around thrice, and with a great show of disgust he thrust his stick into the earth. 'There' he said. 'It's below here. You are a robber and a scoundrel.'

I pretended I hadn't heard this last insult. 'Now before I let you go, I must have a promise from you sir,' I said. 'That you will not take this stick from the ground.'

Pain creased across the Leprechaun's face. 'Aagh! You have my promise.' He squealed.

'Good enough,' I said. As I let him go a great sudden wind knocked me on my back. When I sat up the Leprechaun was gone, but the stick was still there.

Where I had nipped him between my finger and thumb I had a sore rash as if I had touched a nettle. But that scarcely troubled me. I ran across two fields as if my shirt was on fire, then over the wall and up the boreen to the house. The sunset was on my back. My boots clattered in the yard and there was my spade leaning against the wall by the door. Back, like a hare, down the boreen and over the wall with my spade over my shoulder. Now the big red sunset was in my eyes and lust for the buried treasure was in my heart. I would be a rich man! I would buy new boots, a fine suit of clothes and a big house with roses in the garden and carpet on the floor.

I leapt the wall like an acrobat (I was fast in those days) and across the two fields rapidly closing the distance between me and the braying donkey. There was a lash of sweat on my brow, but I was giddy with fine speculation of the treasure. Gold coins lying in the black earth. The Leprechaun's old hoard of stolen money. Soft, generous gold. Enough to set a man up for life.

I got to the gate and vaulted it, landing in the pasture on two feet. And the groan that came from my throat was like a man dying of disappointment. I stood there with my chest heaving and I threw my spade on the ground in anger. For the field was staked and pricked by ten, twenty, or thirty thousand polished little blackthorn sticks, all exactly the same. The poor old donkey was completely stockaded by them. They were almost as common as the blades of grass. The Leprechaun had kept his promise but he had also tricked me. I couldn't dig up the whole field, so I loped home in despond, and I have never been a rich man.

And that is the story of the evening I met the Leprechaun. Since that day every time I hear a creaking hinge it puts me in mind of that cunning little fellow.'

In four years my grandfather would be dead. He took with him all his delight of the quizzical and the ghostly and the tragic; the sense of a tricksy otherworld, very close to our own. Also the notion of a threshold between these dimensions that was almost casually crossable.

I have had my own encounter with the Leprechaun. When I was in my early twenties I left a friend's house in the early hours of the morning. We had been drinking. I was staying back with my parents for a few weeks. My friend's house was down towards the sea on a very grand avenue, with trees all along the centre. New street lights had been installed but as it was after midnight it was almost pitch black. I was singing to myself to keep my spirits up, for I have always been afraid of the dark.

As I neared the top of the avenue I saw a light to my right. That was Jefferies Lane which led to some old flint walled houses that had been surrounded by 1930's villas. There was one iron street lamp there from an earlier age. I still have no idea why this one lamp was still lit when all the others were dark. I walked on past the lane but had a great bolt of sudden shock when I saw a little man dancing in the yellow compass of the light. I stopped quite still, but every muscle in me shouted that I should run like the wind all the way home. There he was dancing in the light, his tiny face looking straight at me. His white socks flicked in a quick step jig.

In an instant I saw that it was an illusion. It was, in fact, a cat running towards me. The dancing flash of the Leprechaun's socks were the cat's white paws. It might seem daft but for a second I really had believed I had seen the Leprechaun.

A few years ago I related this story to an old academic who has made a great reputation in the study of folklore and myth. I explained that my belief was that at the moment of panic, I drew on the stories I had been given as a child in a kind of unbidden archetypal fashion. The woman smiled and said, 'How do you know that it wasn't really the Leprechaun and that he turned into a cat as soon as he noticed you looking at him?'

Child Roland

You must first pass the sentry geese. How they clack and hiss on the quilt of green meadow that slants up to Coombes Church. The tapsel gate spins on a central pivot, so that when you enter the graveyard its other half opens to the world and closes back on your heels in a completed curve. From the trees comes only rusty crow chatter. The Saxons liked their chapels to be intimate, and Coombes is suitably tiny, so it takes no more than thirty seconds to trail your fingers along all sides of the slick flint walls. You are back at the porch before there is time to think. Would that it had been this way for Burd Ellen all those years ago.

Daffodil yellow laughter in the green meadow. A boy and girl are playing at ball. 'Duff' is the sound it makes when it is kicked. Burd Ellen is older than Roland. They both have chestnut hair, but she is tall and her shadow licks long across the grass. They would call the boy Roland a 'kiddy' here in Sussex, meaning not that he is a child, but instead that he has yet to go out into his wide future. His sister too is nearly a woman.

'Duff', the ball pitches down to Roland. He laughs in the May morning, and he kicks it high. Over his sister's head it flies. Over the tapsel gate and then high, high into the blue above the church roof. Burd Ellen yaahs him for an oaf and hitches her skirts. She runs up to the gate. Her shadow reaches the rails before she does. Then she is through the gate, with her long hair streaming as she runs to the back of the church.

13

Roland waits but Ellen does not re-appear. After a minute he calls her name. Then he calls it again. Nothing. Just the elms creaking and the wind soughing. Nothing. Then he too pushes the gate, which spins and nearly catches the back of his legs.

He runs past the porch and into the shadow on the north side and sees nothing. Nothing save long grass parting in the wind and white irises, and beyond the graveyard bare downland where the sheep graze. She has gone, snapped out of the day completely.

Then it comes to him – widdershins! She ran the wrong way, against the course of the sun! Widdershins. He wheels about and calls her name, although he knows she is not there. He bolts away from the church, across the downs. An hour later and bent double with wheezing, he is on top of the giant hill that was a fort before the Romans came. The sea is distant to his back. The wind blusters loud. He looks across the hills to a coven of trees hunching on the horizon. Smoke wavers above the trees.

Merlin's hut is wattles and slubbed clay. Smoke seeps from chinks and cracks in the walls, and out of the door. Smoke fumbles up to a mossy hole in the roof. Merlin lives alone on top of Chanctonbury. People leave him be. Roland once brought him mushrooms. He is not afraid of the old man, for all his odd blether and scratching.

'Widdershins?' Merlin coughs. Between his fingers he rubs thyme and lovage into a boiling pot. 'By Cerunnos and Aeron, why?'

Grave Merlin with his twig-threaded beard, his bare ankles and flapping cloak. His eyes seem to spin crazy when Roland looks into them, like mackerel lures paid out into the past. Old eyes. Winter eyes.

'Has Adze-Head made the sign on your brow?' Merlin's accent is strange, not from here.

'What?'

'Ach, the Adze-Head – the Priest!' Merlin sputters with irritation. 'Did the priest bless you when you were a baby?'

'Yes, we were all christened.' Roland can hardly breathe for the smoke in the hut.

'Widdershins. Your mother often told you and your father too, before they died. Told you not to run widdershins around the church.' Merlin's voice is all up and down. 'She has been stolen. Taken by the King of Elfland into his Dark Tower.'

'Where', Roland asks, 'is this dark tower?'

'Far away.'

'How are we to rescue her?' Roland's eyes stream with smoke and anguish.

'Christendom.' Merlin's accent is like a crust of snow breaking. Like a cough before a song.

'What?'

'Only the boldest knight in Christendom can rescue your sister Burd Ellen.'

Ham is Roland's hot-headed eldest brother. He back-hands the boy across the room where he falls in a clatter of pewter and treen bowls. In his rage he calls Roland every name he can think of for not taking care of their only sister. Just as Ham is unbuckling his belt to give Roland another lash Aelfred, the next oldest, steps between them. 'Peace, Ham. Peace.'

'Peace?' Shouts Ham, his mouth is like a red forge. His temples are crimson. 'I must away to the Dark Tower to find our Burd Ellen. Make sure the boy does not lead you, too into peril.' Ham grabs a hazel stick and walks to the door.

'Boldest knight in Christendom. Pah!' He gives Roland a furnace look and is gone.

They wait. All through the summer they look to the chalk path that Ham trod into the woods. He never returns.

When the harvest is in and the cattle are in the winter byre Aelfred begins to grow restless. Aelfred, the handsome one whose name indeed means Elf- Kissed.

One day Roland finds his brother stuffing bread and cheese into a bag. Aelfred hoists the bag over his shoulder. 'I am off to find Ellen and Ham. I do not know if I am the boldest knight in Chris-

15

tendom, but I must try to rescue them.' Fair and gainly, Aelfred walks the chalk path into the woods, over the hill.

He doesn't return.

Roland stands on the springy downland grass outside Merlin's door. 'Gyre and gyre,' the old man laughs. 'I have stepped into your story. Come along inside.'

Roland sits on the bare earth floor, his chin resting on his knees. The wizard faces him from the other side of his crackling fire. 'How do I get to the Dark Tower?' He asks.

'Any direction will take you to Elfland, but you may as well walk the path your brothers took.'

'You said it was far away. How far?'

'Very far.'

'How will I know the place when I see it?'

'You will know when you draw near to the Dark Tower.' Merlin stirs his bubbling pot.

'Well I must go.' He rises, but Merlin stretches his arm fast and grips Roland's wrist in his long tight fingers.

'Wait. There is more.' Merlin's grey eyes fix him.

'What more?'

'Only the boldest knight in Christendom can rescue your sister.'

'I know that.'

'Well, if you make it to the realm of the King of Elfland you must eat nothing and drink nothing. When you are in his realm you must speak to all who you meet. However, you must then kill all to whom you speak.'

Roland swallows hard. 'Kill?'

Long fingers tighten around Roland's wrist. 'Yes, behead them.' Then Merlin reaches up to the rafters of his hut and takes down a long, smoke-blackened sword. 'Here,' he says in his wheedling rasp. 'This was your father's. He gave it to me and told me to give it to you. This is a sword that never strikes in vain.'

16

Roland stands with the too-big-for-him sword. 'Is this all?'

'All?' Merlin's eyebrows rise high up on his forehead. 'All, he says! All? Let me tell you, boy, the King of Elfland is a fearsome fellow to go against. He is bitter and hard. Suppose you win through to his dark tower, you will find a cunning and merciless enemy.'

Roland stands, a youthful and naive haughtiness flushes him. 'Is this all?'

'Yes. Go.' Merlin rubs sage and thyme into his simmering pot.

'Just one more question.'

'What?'

'Are you making a spell in that pot?'

'No, it is my dinner.'

On the brow of the hill of trees called Chanctonbury, Roland shoulders the long blade and pauses. He turns back to look, but Merlin's hut is gone, as if it had never been.

Inland from the South Down lies the Weald, which in Roland's morning all those years ago is a belt of forest, miles wide, miles deep. His chalk path leads down into the green shuddering light. Small against the first trunks, Roland soon passes among the tall oak tribe and is lost.

He walks until his legs are sapped. He walks until the day begins to dim. He sleeps in a ferny hollow and awakes to shake off the leaves and insects. He walks the forest alone with only the litter of unseen birdsong in his ears. He sleeps and wakes again.

Days pass in the forest. He walks until his shoes split open. He leaves the forest and skirts a great grey lake in the shadow of a high mountain. He climbs the mountain, leaning on the sword when the fatigue overcomes him. Weeks pass and still he tramps the track. His chestnut hair grows long around his shoulders. He never looks behind in case his heart fails him. His eyes are forever narrowed to the way ahead. The wind whistles into his eyes. He walks until there comes a time when all he knows is that he must walk and his sister is only a grudging memory in the deep of his mind.

One day at sunset he walks across bare, gravelly ground and

finds a place to sleep on the banks of a stream that flows away into a cleft between the rocks. He awakes to a dim dawn and rouses himself as he has done a hundred times before.

A cool wind blows the dock leaves away from him as he begins his journey and the half-light seems to prickle his skin. He walks for an hour but the pearly morning grows no brighter. There is no sun in the blank low sky, but far to the north a handful of pale stars glimmer.

Roland looks about himself and notices how darkly green and luscious the foliage has become. How slow the breeze feels on his face, and he begins to realise that he must have passed into Elfland.

He walks through a sweep of buttercups and up into a cleared pasture. Horses graze there. Horses the like of which Roland has never seen before. Beautiful white creatures, with red manes and silver hooves. They have necks like swans and tipping spouts of milk as they bend to the deep emerald grass.

In the midst of the horses stands a herdsman with a clutch of halters in his hands. 'Here, sir,' says the boy breathlessly. 'I have come to find the king of Elfland.' He is relieved at last, after so many weeks on the road alone, to meet someone. The herdsman faces him. There is a steady champ as the horses pitch and dip. The stranger is clothed in rags the colour of new nettles. His face is dark under his hood, but his eyes glitter like sixpences in a well. He says nothing, but he holds out his hand and a red shiny apple sits in the palm.

'No thank you sir.' Roland's shrunken stomach yearns for the apple. 'Where is your king's dark tower?'

The herdsman turns away and in a voice as bleak as grey sleet he says, 'I don't know.'

Roland looks across the pasture and sees a gap in the spinney, where his path leads. He goes to walk on, but stops when he re-members the sword on his shoulder. His father's sword; the sword that never fails. The herdsman is still standing with his green back

18

to him. Roland grunts but the blade whispers, and in a blink, a breath, a twitch, the stranger's head rolls into the grass.

Beyond the spinney is a hedge with a heavy gate. Roland swings the gate and enters a field where the wet clover reaches his thighs. Cows of the like he has never seen before raise their heads. They are great tall beasts, white with splashes of red across their flanks, like bloody banners. Their ears twitch redly and their wide horns are silver. When they start lowing the clover spills from their slack mouths.

A cowherd in a green cloak, hardly older than Roland himself, steps through the cattle. He smiles broadly and swishes the grass with his stick. His hair is red as embers and his eyes glitter silver like scraped salmon scales. He says nothing but offers a piece of yellow cheese to the famished traveller.

Roland declines, although for an instant his hand half reaches for food. 'Where is the King's dark tower?' He asks the smiling boy.

A troubled change like a melting candle passes across the face of the cowherd. He turns away and in a voice as sour as spoilt milk he says, 'I don't know.'

The blade never fails. A whistle in the morning. A slick polishing arc. A scything tear underneath the wind and the cowherd's head leaps from his body. Roland walks on.

By a bank of bluebells a cottage of rough slapped daub stands with a crazy chimney. Next to the hovel is a yard where chickens pick. Roland has never seen fowl such as these. The cockerel's comb is silver. His spurs glint like red thorns. Boldly white is this little emperor's plumage. Around him his crimson hens scratch with beaks like silver clasps.

A henwife in a tattered green bonnet is tending the chickens. She casts yellow vetch flowers and seeds across the yard. She is as twisted as an old yew and as she looks up at Roland, her eyes glitter silver like new cobbler's tacks. She smiles toothlessly and reaches into her patched coat. She holds out an egg, newly boiled and peeled. Roland's hunger cries in his belly, in his legs and his mouth, but he shakes his head.

He places the tip of his sword into the gravel at his feet and coughs, 'I am seeking the king of Elfland and his Dark Tower. Can you give me the direction?'

The henwife's face seems to crumple inwards like an old leather bucket, but she nods and raises her arm. Her hand is like a clump of fresh-dug burdock root. She points a crooked finger and says, 'That way.' Her voice is dry, dry as an ungreased hinge, as though she hasn't spoken for a long, long time.

Roland draws a small circle in the gravel with the point of his blade. 'How far?'

'Not far.'

'How do I enter the Dark Tower?'

The henwife shifts from one leg to the other. She groans. 'You must say three times "Open door!" Then she turns her back to him and pulls the green bonnet over her face. Roland sees that she has dropped the seeds and yellow vetch flowers, as if she knows what is coming.

Sweep, snick, sheer. Keen as ice water bites the blade that never fails. Roland leaves the henwife's head rolling towards a bowl where the chickens drink.

So Roland follows the slant of the old woman's direction and this leads him across some scrubby hills where ox-eye daisies nod at him in the thick air. At last he comes to a stone wall and over it he sees a narrow valley just like the one he left in Sussex all those weeks ago.

Just like? No. Instead of a Saxon chapel, in its place stands a green mound, grown all over with knotted brambles. The light, such as it is, has grown so murky that the mound looks as if it is choked below stagnant pond water. When he comes to stand before it he marvels that it is only twice his height. He walks around it and quickly arrives back at the place of his own beginning. So is this the Dark Tower?

He looks for a door, but all is wet grass and nodding brambles. Chestnut-haired, like a colt, and made small against the weight of his father's sword, Roland takes a deep breath and shouts wildly,

'Open door! Open door! Open door!'

The mound shudders. Clods of grass tumble from the mound. There is a grinding clamour below Roland's feet and the centre of his vision is suddenly blurred. A cold wind comes, a shrieking wind that plays his ears badly. Soil and stones spatter his face, his arms, his chest. He throws down his father's sword and stands before the rending earth, rubbing his eyes and muffling his ears.

When the wind tails away Roland rubs the flung dirt from his face and looks up. Above and through and in the mound, but not of it, has risen a glassy black tower, yet tiny, as if seen from a great distance. It stands for an instant – arches, buttresses and turrets, all picked in sharp lustre, then it fades and Roland sees that the mound is open. A stone lintel, all spiral-carved, frames a black passage into the ground.

When the boy crosses the threshold he is stung by a chill catching his neck and a gust that passes over him like a sigh. Darkness. Now he walks a blind and narrow passage. The polished floor slopes downwards, as slick as a frozen stream. He touches the close walls and his fingers graze etched lines that flow forward, ever forward. He treads unlit, eyes gaping on the dark, like passing into a fearful sleep.

He has walked for weeks to find the door into the Dark Tower, but now he walks until he forgets that he is walking. He forgets his eyes. He forgets his own name. The memory candles of his sister and two brothers have guttered out. He still holds the sword that never fails, his father's sword, but he has forgotten it. He wades the darkness and for all he knows years could be sweeping by him. He walks . . .

. . . Until, at the end of the black, down in the very deep, after his timeless pacing, Roland's sword scrapes against a door. He trips and falls against it. The door swings open and he staggers shivering and wordless into the hall of the Elf King.

The vault of the roof rears into gloom. The floor, like the sheet of a black lake, skates away from him to a throne between two pillars of stone. And his sister, Burd Ellen, is seated there. His sister, who was forgotten on his long trek downwards.

Her name breaks from his lips. He runs to her across the fathoms of the shining floor. When Burd Ellen sees him she stands and steps down from her dais. She wears a velvet gown, the colour of mulberries, such a garment as she could never have hoped to wear in the mortal world. At her throat is a silver pendant. It flashes as she rises. He draws near and sees, not joy, but a pinch of pain in her face, as if she is snared in a burl of thorns. 'You should not have come.' Her voice is lower than the voice he knew. There are tears in it.

'I have come to save you.' He reaches his fingers towards her, but she shakes her head.

'Brother, this cannot be.' Burd Ellen retreats to the dais. 'You must go back, before the King finds you here.'

'But I have come so far. I cannot go back without you.'

'You must.' The pale look of pain seems to be growing on her face. Roland feels his legs giddying and finds that his head has become as light as kindled leaf. Thirsty. He realises that he has not drunk a drop since he entered Elfland.

'Water.' His voice is dry as ashes.

Burd Ellen looks at him with her tear-heavy gaze and turns to a silver ewer. She pours water and hands him a wide earthen cup. He takes it and looks down into the water. His face billows there, haggard and famished. Cold water, like the spring near Coombes, where the water will numb your teeth and slice any thirst.

His sister waits as Roland raises the bowl. Spring water, like the icy cry of a hawk on the Downs above Coombes. Spring water, like a spear of memory. Spring water. Merlin's words!

Burd Ellen screams as Roland dashes the cup to the floor and it jumps into many shards.

'Go,' she begs. 'I am held here by a spell of the King, but you must go.'

Before Roland can reply, at the far end of the hall, a door flies

22

clean from its hinges and in bursts the King. Fast he is, like a long black hound. He leaps across the floor and his eyes glitter like shattered flint, like beetle shell, like ink on a silver nib. He cries at Roland in a strange language, all upside-down and back-sprung.

And then he is upon him. When the Elf King strikes, Roland is tossed in the air like an empty jacket. He lands in a clump and his father's sword, the blade that never fails, skitters away on the polished floor.

The King rages at him again. White face, like a youth. Old eyes and black curls. Such fury, as he works his red mouth. A back-handed swipe and Roland is flung to the steps of the dais. The Elf King stands over him. His armour is as black as a swallowing, moonless night. His tingling, piercing, unintelligible words glance every shining surface, but there are no echoes in his Dark Tower. He raises his right hand and a flock of silver darts rain from the unseen roof. He spreads his left hand and the throne frets into a million splinters. Roland thrashes. His clothes are shredded. He is slashed and pierced.

The king bends. His left fist is drawn back, clenched for a killing blow. His shadow spiders across the youngster. Triumph kindles darkly in his ancient eyes. But Roland swims his arm across the fathomless floor and his fingers reach for the pommel of the sword, his father's sword, the sword that never fails.

Hiss breathes the blade, a wintry curse, a tang of iron. And now Child Roland is up, and the long nip of the sword is at the white throat of the Elf King, and he quails for he cannot abide the forge-chimed steel.

Down he is forced, onto his knees. Bleeding and bruised Roland holds the king fast at one glistening shoulder, for he has found a steady Sussex courage in himself and he sees how his enemy frets under the blade. 'Yield!' he cries. For he remembers how the Sussex men say 'We wun't be druv.'

A smudge of agony passes over the face of the Elf King, and an uncertain look, like an infant roughly woken. He glances to the right and to the left of him.

'Free my sister. Free my two brothers,' commands Roland.

The King's white face is that of a tormented child. He wails in anguish, old wild words, syllables coughed from deep black corners. To Roland they are tongue-thorns; spite-lashes, vex-hatched grudges. Yet at last he submits, trembling, with his black eyes on the long sword that never fails. He opens his mailed fist and stars his fingers. He whispers a quick tracery of sibilance and in an instant he grows dim against the sheen of the floor. Then he is gone. Roland's sword that pricked against Elf flesh now ponders on nothing. All that is left is a flurry of white hawthorn petals floating on the polished onyx floor.

Heaving and shaking, Roland looks to his sister Burd Ellen, who steps from the dais in her mulberry gown with tears like pearls on her cheeks. As she walks between the two stone pillars they smoke and tremble into the forms of the brothers, Aelfred and Ham.

At the far end of the hall a door is ajar. Child Roland drops the blade that never fails and it clangs like a mass bell. The four of them walk outside to a sunlit morning. An oaky slam, a sound fettered with bands of Wealden iron, makes them turn. They see to their astonishment that they have just stepped from the door of the church at Coombes.

How can it be that the King of Elfland's Dark Tower stood unnoticed and masked in the Saxon knapped flints of the church? Child Roland creaks open the latch and pokes his chestnut head into the familiar nave. He sees the murals, the font and the rood screen. The Bible lays shut and clasped on the lectern.

Before they step through the tapsel gate they run the small circuit of the church, letting the wind wash the fug of the under-place of Elfland from their limbs. Their laughter is sieved through yew and elm branches and then into the naked downland air. Burd Ellen runs ahead of her brothers and as she comes back to the porch her mulberry gown fades to original brown.

The astonishment of their deliverance passes from them quickly and they are untroubled by the time they step through the tap-sel gate. All except Burd Ellen. For as the last patch of mulberry scarlet bleeds from her dress, she looks for an instant as if she is struggling to recall a lost dream.

What is certain is that none of them will ever run widdershins around the church again.

However, the next morning the verger is most truly perplexed to find a sword, twisted and strained and mangled, flung into the graveyard among a scatter of white hawthorn petals.

Herne

*I*n high autumn toadstools constellate the woods; red and white, yellow and brown. The leaves lie among them like gloves of the dead.

There is a forest, or the remnant of one, that has been overlaid by county borders – Surrey, Hampshire and Buckinghamshire, but the forest does not know these invisible names – lines decreed by men. There is an oak amongst all the others, swag-girthed, limbs crazily angled, as if it has gone senile and is sprouting against all normal decorum. It is massive and lurches, in mid-stagger, all alone in a clearing. The other trees stand in a circle, as at a respectful distance.

Here and there, pieces of bark have fallen away revealing the white sapwood. One bare patch is so large that it resembles a doorway. Ivory bracket fungus juts like steps up the trunk and one massive beam casts out across the space, making a reaching shadow, even in the crisp noon. Almost a yard along this beam is a worn ring. It looks almost polished, as if a rope was once fastened there and a heavy load swung out across the gap.

This is Herne's Oak. Do not ask me where it stands; I will not tell you. Trees of the same name were planted by Queen Victoria and her playboy son Edward. These were mere fancies; a royal attachment to half-forgotten lore. There have been many famous and illustrious men who have looked for this tree, yet among them all, it was only Will Shakespeare who found it lurking in its musky glade. It was an old oak, even in his time – older, perhaps, than he knew.

The reason that royalty have held the image of this tree so high-ly in their imaginations is that it is reputed to hold a doom for them. If it falls, they and their house will also fall. And because they have never found the true oak, they plant saplings that grow into false totems in and around Windsor Park. Meanwhile, with splendid contempt the true Oak thrives, in a slow, sap-ticking time all of its own, away in a neglected stand of the forest that once covered all England. There have been no axes here. These trees have never flinched at the sound of a saw. All the paths seem to veer away from this relic heartwood.

Let us suppose that, by chance, you do hack your way off the guide book trail, through the bracken and brambles, and get close enough to ponder the corrugated bark, the clawed branches and the ring-burned beam. Keep an eye on the November light as it needles through the woods. Turn away between two and three, before darkness begins to fall. Find the path and do not look back. I know you will. The forest teems with clicks and snaps – the flick of a squirrel, a thrush in a thicket. The evening comes quickly, like a velvet sheet drawn over the bosk. A pheasant jirrs away from you. Its throttled cry tears the dusk. Of course you start. Of course you look behind. It suddenly seems a long way back to the pub car park, the stile and the laminated trail sign.

The sentinel trees stutter the dying light. Stop quite still. Back there in the glade something glints silver, as if a coin has been tossed in the gloaming. And what is that 'notch-notch' sound? A wind comes in the direction of the setting sun. It tries the collar and seams of your jacket. Turn from the wind and face the clearing. You can hear better with your mouth open. No cars hum in the distance, but there now is a heavy thump as a horse places its hoof. Then the unmistakable slink and chomp as it plays with the bit.

So here you are, standing open-mouthed, and there is a horse back there. It is a black and massive beast. You can see its haunch-es fractured by the trees. It is pacing the clearing, pawing the ground, snorting. You sense - rather than see it - bucking its neck.

You hear the trappings of its bridle. You want to cry out, to ask if there is someone there. But for some reason you do not speak. Instead you turn and strive for the path. The cold branches claw on either side. As your eyes begin to grope, fear seems to hiss at you from every cleft and thorn.

'Notch-notch.' You suddenly place the sound. Antlers being sharpened, tested against a tree. It is, after all, autumn – the belling time. The horse continues to pace back there. Horse and stag? You fix on the fading eye of the red sun and aim for the car park half a mile away. Best not to run. You might snag your feet. Suddenly, there comes a yelp and whine of hounds crying in delicious anticipation. They are straining these dogs, their paws aching for the chase. The chase!

You run. Your legs are spurred by an urge so ancient it is deeper than fright. It is nameless and thoughtless. Your body reacts without permission or regard. You are running a narrow track. Twigs pull at your jacket, your hands, your face, but the scratches are painless. Only at the most tremendous crashing do you stop again and turn to look back.

A sight of deepest nightmare breaks from the stand of trees circling the clearing. Such a leaping picture is found only in the dim recesses of caves, where our ancestors splashed their fears across limestone in the colours of blood and charcoal. A stallion, sleek as liquid tar, rears through the saplings, sending beech leaves upwards in a vortex. A rider, booted, bearded, huge, spurs the beast. His sword takes the red of the sun. The stark antlers of a king stag thrust from his head. At his side three dogs, the colour of washed coal, bay the rising moon. Their fangs are white. Their eyes are crimson slits.

You take all this in the second before you turn and hare down the path, running as you have never run before. You are oblivious to the breath itching like rust in your lungs. You are blind to the snares and snatches of cruel wood. In your eyes there is only the lowest bleb of sunset, in your ears only the pounding of massive hooves and the hounds singing for your flesh.

31

Say his name: 'Herne'. It comes like a threat of frost across the tongue. Or a wind that sharps when the rooks pause calling and there should be a silence in the trees. Herne. Scholars have attempted to trace his story back, but the strands of his tale are like a run of weedy ground elder leading ever deeper into the forest. In his play, The Merry Wives of Windsor, Shakespeare gives us a few muscular lines concerning the rider in the woods:

> There is an old tale goes, that Herne the hunter,
> Sometime a keeper here in Windsor forest,
> Doth all the winter time at still midnight,
> Walk around about an oak, with great ragg'd horns;
> And there he blasts the tree, and takes the cattle;
> And makes milch-kine yield blood, and shakes a chain
> In a most hideous and dreadful manner.

It is worth remembering that Will was once fined for poaching deer when he was a youth in Warwickshire. He knew the woods, knew the tawny heart of autumn. Windsor people would have told him the old tale:

> Why, yet there want not many, that do fear
> In deep of night to walk by this Herne's oak.

In the inns they would have told him that many years before, back in King Richard's time, there was a loyal keeper who accompanied his liege on deep forays to hunt boar and stag. One day they tracked spoor to a glade and there they came upon a white hart, ice-kissed and proud in the spring noon. The king drew his bow and shot, but the arrow went wide and caught the stag in the hind quarter. Blood fell on the snowdrops. The hart thrashed and roared. It lowered its tines and charged at the king, who stood transfixed and aghast. A shadow fell across his breast. It was his keeper, who had stepped in front to take the blow. Horn stabbed the keeper's doublet, sheared into his ribs. Again, blood spattered the snowdrops. But he had drawn his dagger and the blade flashed at the stag's white throat. This, they say, was Herne, who lay mortally injured under the hart, and had saved the life of Richard, his king.

They brought him back on the same cart on which the stag was thrown. Some say that a wizard appeared that night and ordered the hart's antlers to be fetched to Herne's bedside. The wizard tied the horns to Herne's head and said that although desperately ill he would heal. Sure enough, within a week he was strong again. The king, ever mindful of his reputation, promoted this Herne to head keeper. He returned to his work now dressed in a fine new hunting livery of deepest green, the envy of all the other keepers. But all was not well. Herne found that all his keen skills of tracking, his knowledge of wind and instinct for the direction of the herds had disappeared. At night he lay in his bed thrashing, as if in a fever. His dreams were all of chase and arrows and blood.

The other keepers, those jealous of his new livery and position, whispered to Richard; within weeks he fell from favour. The king dismissed Herne and banished him from the forest and parkland. Yet still Herne lingered there, particularly after dark, when the deer trod in slow state through the trees, under the white face of the moon. And so it happened that one night the band of keepers found Herne standing alone in the very glade where he had saved the king's life. They seized him, tied his wrists and slipped a noose over his head. They threw the rope over the beam of a sturdy oak at the centre of the glade and they hanged him. Laughing, they watched him kick and then they left his slumped body pendulous under the stars.

The next morning a young swineherd ran to the keepers and told them he had seen a man riding fast through the woods with antlers on his head and a pack of dogs at his heels. They went to the clearing and found an empty noose swinging in the wind.

At the fireside in the taverns the locals would have told Will Shakespeare how Herne's fierce ghost roamed wide across the counties of Hampshire, Surrey and Berkshire, seeking his revenge on all who stand in his way. A particular curse of his is reserved for the descendants of Richard, the monarchs who have fenced and tamed the woods.

The bones of this tale may have been good enough for Will to hang with the sturdy flesh of his poetry, but the story of a horned rider from the depths of the wood seems to have more to it than the revenge of a hanged keeper. Antlers and a fiery steed? A hoary tree and pitch-dark hounds? Like the sneaking tendrils of ground elder that twine along unseen tracks, some people believe that Herne can be followed back much further than King Richard's time, to ancient and unsettling origins.

'Herne'; say the name again. It is like a sudden gust of snow on naked skin, or the trembling minute between two clouts of thunder. There are those linguists who have skills to untangle old languages. They see the name Herne as a worn smooth version of 'Herian', which in turn is derived from the old Norse 'Einherja'. And here the chill begins to prickle at your neck, for 'Einherjar' means 'Leader of the slain' and is one of the guises of Odin the furious, Odin the smiter, Odin the fell god of the wilderness and mountains.

Odin, Wotan, Woden; all across the north of Europe, from the oak to the beech, from the ash to the pine, they used to worship him. When the English came to Britain their gods went before them into the forests and moors. Chief among them was their one-eyed, implacable Woden.

He is restless and vital, known for his trickery and cunning disguises. He has many faces, many forms, including this cold title: 'Hangatyr' – 'God of the Hanged'. Accordingly, there is a verse in the old poem, 'Havamal', that tells of a weird and gruesome consummation:

I know that I hung on a windy tree
nine long nights ...
... myself to myself,
on that tree of which no man knows ...

On the sacred oak Woden sacrificed himself to himself. Pinioned there, he fretted against his own divinity. He was pierced by his own spear. As he hung against the bark, the branches wrapped around his legs and arms. Ivy crawled over his skin and thorns stabbed his flesh. Lost in his agony he looked inwards down the hidden paths of his mind. Then on the ninth night he came down from the tree with knowledge. In the wilderness of his torment he had gained the secrets of the runes. For it was Woden, so our ancestors believed, this God of the Hanged, who brought writing to mankind.

Hunters give clear whistles and shrill cries. They favour brass horns of high clarion. You can shout in a forest and the sound will blunt against the trees. How much more so with whispers? In November the leaves purse on the wind and one man conferring to another will find his tale taken and twisted. Stories pass down through centuries and susurrate against the years. The stories change. A Teutonic hanged god transmutes to a tale of a king, a white hart and a wronged keeper. Yet the sap of the truth can be tapped, and Herne, the 'Leader of the Slain', canters towards us in one more dread aspect.

You are still running. The forest hunches in the smoky new darkness. The roots and branches still hiss at your limbs. The growing weakness in your chest must be denied if you are to gain the car park. Behind you the undergrowth thrashes and the hounds leap every fallen trunk in slavering joy. The horse plunges and the horned rider bends low with his mailed hand open, ready to snatch. He is literally at your heels.

You break onto the tarmac. Your Golf sleeps over by the wall of the pub. There are no lights on; no smoke from the chimney. The pub is closed. It is over. You trip, falling first on one knee, and then you feel the gravel bite your cheek. It is over. A hunted fox will run and run, but sooner or later it will fall, and then, ribs heaving, tongue lolling, it will turn and await the pack.

From the carved gables of the Schwarzwald to shepherd huts in the Tatras Mountains, from rain-soaked cottages in the Cumbrian

Fells to Basque villages under the crags of the Pyrenees there are tales of a relentless huntsman and his pack of hounds. In Germanic and Nordic lands they are known as the Wild Hunt. A horned rider gallops the midnight sky, through bogs and vaulted glens. His prey is any traveller foolish enough to let darkness overtake his steps. More explicitly it is the wicked and those with guilty secrets who have the most to fear.

Everywhere the stories tell that the huntsman rides sinners down in lonely places. He grabs them by the scruff of the neck and carries them up into the shivering heights. The victim dangling at the pommel of the saddle might look behind and see the dogs coursing at their master's side. How they yelp and gnash in ecstasy. Behind them he might see other riders – gaunt figures with parchment skin and dreadful eyes. Moonlight picks out their horned helmets and tarnished breastplates. The dead ride in Herne's train. He is, after all, 'Einherjar' – the Leader of the Slain. The victim is bound for hell.

The stallion rears over you and when its hoof comes down sparks flash on the frosty gravel. You are on your back cringing. Your jacket is torn. The rider leans towards you across his creaking saddle. His horse snorts and shudders. He holds the dogs back with a sweep of one gauntlet. They snap and growl in disappointment. His black beard is woven with ivy. His antlers are fluttering velvet rags. His eyes hold nothing. They are empty. He speaks but no words are audible. His speech comes in an icy furl. He shouts noiselessly and sudden rime crackles on your scratched cheek. Then comes a moment more awful than all the preceding ones. He fixes you with his oblivion stare and sharp silence creeps over you. You cannot think. Terror floods your ears, your mouth. Say whatever prayers you can remember.

He straightens and looks about himself, looks up to the new stars. He points with his red sword and suddenly kicks his spurs. The horse rears again, but this time it does not descend. Instead it lifts. Impossibly the horse gallops upwards, bearing the huntsman over the tiled roof of the pub. The hounds follow, chasing on the air above your head. Their eager baying fades on the wind. Herne does not want you. You have been lucky.

St Dunstan and the Devil

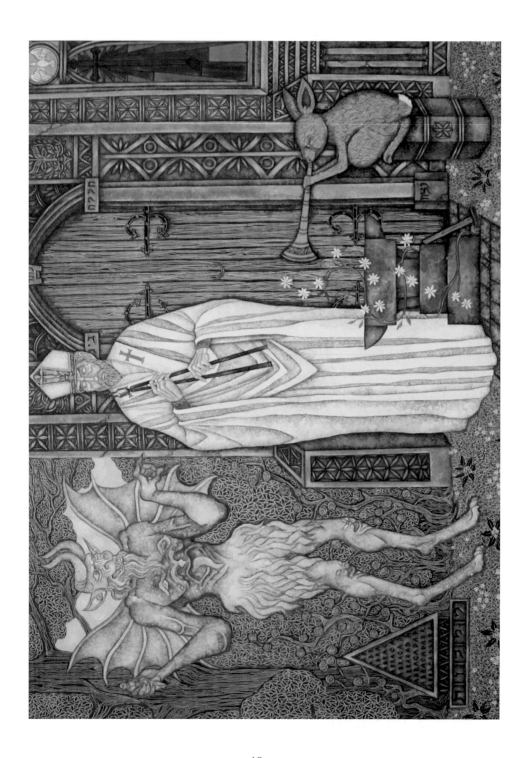

40

*S*t Dunstan is fissling in his smithy. Tinkering and tapping, he sits in a shaft of cool sunlight. His hair is pale yellow, like harvest-time wheat.

He squints one of his eyes as he tools a rectangle of red goat-skin that will go to make the binding of a copy of the gospel – which is written in good brawny old Wessex English, no less – *Faeder ure thu the eart on heofonum, si thin nama gehalgod.* And so too, in-tones St Dunstan as he goes about his work. He has already made the edgings for the book in gold and garnet. These lie scattered over his bench, glinting amid the chisels, scraps, awls and bodkins.

Tendril and interlacing – St Dunstan has given twining life to the leather. He has copied the gospel onto new vellum, and painted each page with sprightly pictures: long-bearded disciples meshed in the calligraphy, fully fledged angels and dogs whose tongues weave into an inky thicket of coils at the borders of each page. Here is a living, speaking book taking shape, made to shout and chuckle and sing The Word to the people of Sussex. St Dun-stan sits up and stretches. He reaches for an apple cake.

There are a handful of these raw-legged monks scattered across the country; learned, scruffy men, padding the tracks, living among the people, sharing their food, cajoling them, thumbing invisible signs of salvation on their foreheads.

Few places are as remote as Sussex in this, the tenth century af-ter the birth of the Christ. It was the last place in England to accept the Faith. The county is hemmed by marshes on either side. The people are cussed and straight. One of St Dunstan's angels flying across the miles of this landscape would see only the green swathe of thick forest running up towards the northern hills. Just the odd ferule of smoke shows where the little settlements are scattered among the green. Oak and Iron; a monk will be swallowed and marooned among the musky trees.

They wear the new religion lightly here, like a fresh suit of clothes, only to be put on for special occasions. November is blod monath, the blood month, where they light fires to hold back the coming darkness and remember the animal sacrifices their grand-fathers made. Homes are hung with living green at the midwin-ter feast and a great log is burned and they still keep wassail in the New Year, singing to their apple trees. Days of the week are named for the old gods; Tiw, Woden, Thunor, Freja. When they do build churches they carve the beam bosses with the grinning faces of green men who are set there to guard the sacred space. All is oak in these little churches, which are creaking ships of faith in an ocean of leaves. Wooden pegs hold everything in place. But the thick doors are banded with strong black Wealden iron.

Yet the South Saxons love St Dunstan, who has come from the west at the order of far-off king Aethelstan. They love his silver smithying, and his enamelling. They do not understand his strange alphabet, but they love the menageries and apostles he draws in the margins of his books. When he preaches in the church at Mayfield, they love his magical story of the carpenter Jesus who was nailed to a tree and yet came back again through the mists of death to tell them of his father who lives beyond the sun.

If St Dunstan can be accused of any particular sin it is that he is often too absorbed in his crafty work to take no-tice of the everyday affairs of the people of Mayfield. Long after the particular events that I am relating, he feels that he should have heeded the hints and rumours far earli-er and so taken measures to nip things in the bud, as it were.

For instance there was a young boy called Garland who told

42

him that all the unpicked blackberries had turned mushy on the morning of 10th October. Then another boy called Clapshoe, who brings him a fresh loaf each day, said that someone had told him that a swineherd over in Heathfield was out nutting and had met a tall stranger. He was reaching for the cobs when the man appeared on the other side of the hazel tree. Smiling, the stranger held one of the most loaded branches down for him, so that he could fill his bag. When the swineherd looked up to thank him, the stranger was nowhere to be seen.

... Anyway, I am asking you to see St Dunstan now, sitting at his bench, surrounded by all sorts of clutter. His little forge is only just awake; the slinking coals are orange in a dark corner. He is happy that no one has come to look in on him this morning. Often he jumps with a start to find a curious villager standing at his door, silently watching him as he goes about his work. St Dunstan scratches his tonsure and nibbles his cake. The shutters are open and he can see a patch of woods leading down to the stream where he goes to wash. His coarse habit is rucked up to his knees. The stool creaks. Crows carp. Golden leaves pare away on the wind. Wood is being chopped in the distance. St Dunstan drinks the autumn air.

The corn is in and the people are salting their bacon flitches. He has the sudden feeling that everything is being held in the balance, just as it should be. Then, being a man of honest piety, he regrets his momentary pleasure that no one has come visiting, and he whispers a silent prayer of repentance.

'Goistering' is a Sussex word for loud feminine laughter. Scarcely has the prayer died on the monk's lips when he is astonished to hear his name being called just outside the workshop in a voice like a whole set of silver cutlery being dropped down a well. 'St Dustin! St Dustin! St Dustiiiin!' He turns to the doorway. For a second the morning light is eclipsed. 'Hellooo, St Dustin?'

Quickly he pulls his brown habit down over his pale legs. There are crumbs all over his stubbly chin.

'St Dustin? Ah, there you are.' Hand on one hip, laughing and sashaying, in comes a woman, the like of which he has never seen before. The rustle of fallen leaves accompanies her as she sways. St Dunstan is dumbfounded and swallows hard. Because the sun is at her back she appears at first as a series of disjointed fragments, dazzling and flickering. What he does notice immediately is an abundance of golden flesh.

St Dunstan opens his mouth. 'Err?' he says.

'Oh listen to your voice. Such a lovely sound. Everywhere I go they say St Dustin is so sophisticated, so cultured, so learned.' The woman brushes black hair way from her face; it tumbles across her shoulders. Her eyes are silvery-grey like the dawn glimmer across the Rother.

'Err?' replies the monk. His tongue is dry and his heart hammers.

'Hear him speak!' She laughs and her red mouth opens wide. 'Oh, you beautiful man.'

St Dunstan is many things, but he has never been called beautiful. He has a kind of scratchy, end-of-the-garden look about himself. He looks best in a shed. He knows he smells like freshly peeled mushrooms. At last he is surprised to hear some words tumble from his lips. 'Madam,' he says, 'I don't believe we have ... er - that is - I don't think I ... er.'

The woman silences him by holding up one finger. 'No,' she says. 'You were going to ask my name. But that is not important and so I shan't tell you. So just sit still and let me look at you, and then I'll tell you why I came.'

He feels a strange flush come over him and his lips are locked. He sits. The 'looking' seems to be more for St Dunstan's benefit than hers, for she taps across the workshop and stands before him. She is wearing a dress the colour of crimson dogwood leaves. It stretches over her body like a rumpled sheet. She smiles and is quiet. Her black hair is glossed like simmering pitch. You couldn't be a man, and an artist to boot, and not gaze at this woman in wonder.

Therefore, monk as he is, it is as an artist and a man that he takes in the beam of his visitor. Her skin is like pear wood that has been stained to a dull gloss with beeswax. He notices how she is never still and when she moves it puts him in mind of a jar full of honey pouring slowly to the floor. And like golden honey, the light seems to shine through her skin.

'Oh, St Dustin you are everything that I hoped you to be,' she says. He can't place her breathy accent at all. It is like mead infused with faraway spices. She backs away and suddenly springs up to sit on a table. Her dress is slashed to the thigh. The monk looks down the long yard of her legs and sees how tiny her feet are, with shiny black shoes tapering to sharp points. Here is a woman for whom you would kick down a door. As if reading his thoughts, she rolls her eyes and her laughter clashes across the room. 'Good. Let us talk.'

St Dunstan feels his tongue suddenly loosened. 'Since you will not introduce yourself, tell me, what can I do for you?'

'See here' says the woman. He motions to her neck and there he sees a pendant. She reaches for the clasp and undoes the necklace. St Dunstan feels a throbbing at his temples. He must not look there, yet his eyes are fixed on the darkening amber shadows that lead down the low-cut front of her dress. His eyes widen as if his lids will tear at the corners when she bends forward and hands him the pendant. He feels it hot and heavy, but he cannot take his gaze away from the semi-furled secret bosom. 'It is broken,' she says.

Relieved to be able to look anywhere but 'there', he stares at his palm and finds a small silver spider sitting with its legs splayed out to make a claw. The eyes are six tiny rubies. It is an exquisite but cruel object. The woman folds her hands over his and when she touches him a sapling tremor runs through his arm. 'See my little spider. He is broken. One of his legs has gone. I have come a long, long way to find you, so you can fix him.'

'Where are you from?' asked St Dunstan.

Again that laughter. 'Ha ha, from the back of the moon,' she replies. 'Why does it matter where I am from, silly man? I have walked all of the twittens and wappleways to search for the great

St Dustin.'

'It's very delicate work. I – er – that is – I don't think I want to . . .' He is trying to refuse this commission, for he notices that the woman has broken up once more into a series of parts. He doesn't know if it is his imagination, or the sunlight shuttering across the dark of his workshop, but he feels suddenly feverish.

Here are her legs mixed up with her wide smile. Here is her tossed-back chin, her black hair and always shadow between her breasts. St Dunstan feels that a man could place his hand on the ebb and flow of this woman and the glide would never end.

She has drawn close to him. 'You can't refuse. I can pay you.' Her breath smells of cinnamon and it is like nettle rash on his neck.

'What will you pay?' he croaks. She has squeezed his fist so tightly the silver spider's remaining legs have broken the skin of his palm, so he is relieved when she draws away from him. Standing, she tip-tip-taps on her little black shoes and puts one hand back on her hip. He sees her whole again.

Her silver eyes do not blink. 'Here is a little knot that keeps my dress safely tied. I have only to loosen this and it will fall to my ankles. Imagine that, St Dustin. Yes, think of that.'

The monk is off his stool. His brown habit folds in woolly clumps around his ferrety frame. In her heels the woman is a head taller than he is. There is a fire in his cheeks. He feels his shiny tonsure redden and he trembles.

'You are earth and I am fire,' she croons. 'You are an artist. What could you do with this?' She traces the glissade of her curves with her painted fingers.

St Dunstan walks towards the woman. Men have gone to the gallows with less sense of purpose. He imagines the taste of her skin and the arching of her naked back. Her eyes are nearly closed as he draws near. 'Ah, perhaps you would like to loosen this knot yourself.' Her whisper is like a midnight promise that darkens the noon light. She thrusts her hips like a dancer against his bony pelvis. Her little shiny shoes make a slow timpani on the tiles. He looks down at them.

Hesitantly, St Dunstan, Aethelstan's holy monk, the tinkering craftsman, loved by the Sussex people, puts his arm around the cinched waist of the crimson-dressed woman and she leans towards him with her red lips parted ...

Imagine you are standing outside the monk's little workshop. You hear a scalding shriek as if a fox has slammed its paw in the hen house door. It is a sound that fetches the bile up to eat at your teeth. This is the jagged scream that breaks from the lips of the woman. For St Dunstan has reached behind her to his forge, where his favourite heavy tongs have been lying in the live coals all morning. And with these he has firmly nipped her nose between tow tangs of red-hot iron.

'How dare you come here with all your hussying tricks,' he shouts, as the woman squirms and tries to wrestle with the hissing tongs.

'Aiyee St Dustin! What are you doing? Ay, my lovely nose!'

'Stop that,' he cries. 'Your shoes have given you away.' For of course what St Dunstan has noticed is how those little pointy black heels have wavered for a second in his sight and showed themselves to be two neat, lacquered, tapping, cloven hoofs.

With a tug he pulls the screaming woman this way and that. 'Now, now now, enough of all your clitter-clatter says St Dunstan, grunting with the effort. 'You must come forth and show yourself, for as you know,' (tug, tug, tug) 'for as you know, I have you fast pinned by this Sussex iron and you must COME FORTH!' At this he gives the woman's nose such a wrench he half-expects it to come clean off.

'Oh the pain, the cruelty. Yo me estoy muriendo!' Tears like gledes of lead run down her cheeks and blister St Dunstan's hands. Yet now she spasms and convulses and then she is swallowed by a cloud of choking sulphur. St Dunstan feels a great counter-pull, but he hangs on for dear life and squeezes the pincers even tighter. The sulphur blinds him for a second but when he opens them there, cringing rudely and red at the end of his tongs, is the Devil

47

himself, squawking and retching and whining.

'Unhand me!' The Devil is attempting to give a show of haughty outrage, but this is difficult with burning iron clasping your nostrils. 'I am a Prince, for goodness' sake. There are certain protocols, dues and privileges. Oh I beg of you, do let go old boy.'

'We have no use for princes such as you in Sussex,' roars St Dunstan (and who would have thought such a grizzly monk could labour so with the tongs). 'I'll ask you now, why did you come here? When as you well know all the land from South Harting to Rye, and from Newhaven to Rusper is barred to you forever - with the exception of Crawley.'

'Ah, Crawley,' said the Devil. Despite the pain, a look almost of happy reminiscence passes over his crimson face.

'Why?' insists St Dunstan, twisting the tongs again. There is a tremendous racket now in the workshop as the Devil is dragged around, for his tail whisks everything off shelves and benches.

'Ouch, ouch, ouch,' responds the Devil. 'You know why I came - for your laundered, starched, crisp and neatly folded soul.'

'You shan't have it,' yells St Dunstan, panting with the effort. 'What were you thinking of, appearing as a woman like that? What if I had given in? Imagine the gossip!' The Devil's knees suddenly buckle and now the breathless monk is standing over him.

There he is lying on the floor with his red jacket torn and the buttons of his waistcoat popping off as little glinting cinders. His crimson bow tie is all puckered and loose. He tries to smile, although - as you know - the Devil hates his clothes to be rumpled and mired. St Dunstan glimpses the sharp teeth and forked tongue.

'Look here,' says the Devil. He is trying to wrestle his head away. 'I realise there has been a mistake. A good man like you was never going to fall for my old hidalgo act. I see that now. Really I do. So if you'll just let me go, perhaps we could have a pint of Harvey's like proper gentlemen … possibly over a game of cards?'

'None of that!'

'Then maybe a pinch of my puffball fungus snuff? You'll find it in my waistcoat.'

'No,' replies St Dunstan, Aethelstan's man. 'For all your yammering, I mean to wring submission and promise out of you.'

It is now that St Dunstan really begins to go to work. Never has the Devil been subjected to such twisting, hauling agony. He is stricken and buckled and wracked. He begins to cough up gobs of flame. All the while he moans like a wrestler caught in a headlock who is refusing to give in. 'No. No. No.'

'You must yield to me and swear that you will never darken us with your wicked ways again.' By one way or another St Dunstan has dragged the Devil to the door of his workshop. How he cringes and yowls. 'Or I swear by this iron that your princely nose will never be the same again.'

'Very well. Very well. Pax!' gasps Devil, with his voice hoarse and broken.

'Good. Now swear upon all the grim glories of your under-kingdom that you will leave us unmolested forever.'

'Yes, yes, yes. I swear,' hisses the Devil.

St Dunstan unclappers his tongs and stands back. The Devil – dishevelled, despoiled and well-nigh dis-nosed – arises from the dust of the yard. He straightens his collar and smooths his centre-parting. Gingerly and limping slightly on his shiny hooves, the Prince of Darkness steps away and unfurls his wings. He looks long and moodily at the monk. However, St Dunstan knows that even the Lord of Hell is bound by his own promises.

'No class,' spits the Devil. Then he flies off towards Tunbridge Wells to cool his sore nostrils in the waters there (which incidentally is the reason why that drink they peddle just over the Kent border tastes so sulphurous and ghastly).

St Dunstan casts aside his tongs and leans against the door jamb. His scratchy brown habit is soaked with sweat. His arms are quivering like rushes. His workshop is a chaos of tools and broken wood and torn vellum. Yet he is happy that he has foiled the old Trickster with good iron and blessed fire from Wealden

49

charcoal.

As he gathers himself there comes a skittering click from under an overturned chair. He looks down to see a quick flash of silver. It is the broken spider pendant making a dash for the door. Across the floor it darts into the open air. Clapshoe, the boy who brings St Dunstan bread, is surprised to find the exhausted monk stamping and hopping around the yard, and beating the ground with a stick.

St Dunstan never did catch the Devil's pendant, for it escaped into the grass at the edge of the woods. So despite his promise never to trouble the people of Sussex again, the Devil left a tiny part of himself here and for that, we have always to be on our toes.

Wayland

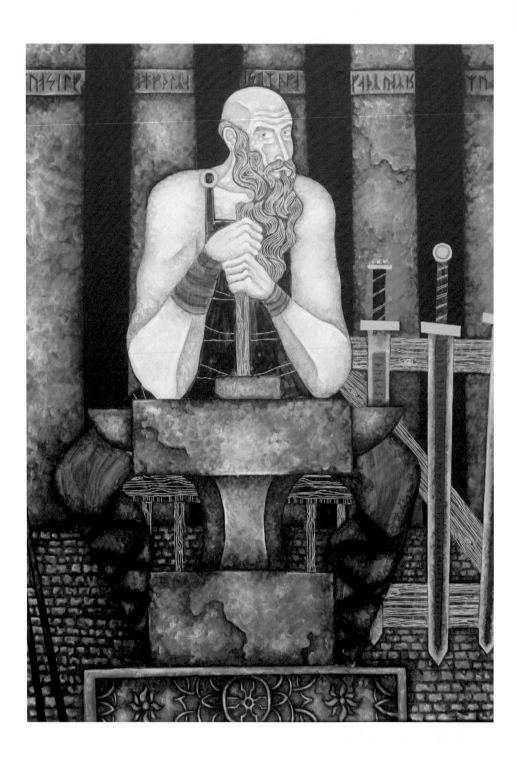

*T*here is a galloping horse etched on the green downland at Uffington. There is something of the sleek hound in its spine stretched leap; something of the dragon in its nipped face. Something of a dream creature, with its un-joined legs. No one knows who carved this sinuous morning stallion. Was it the emblem of some ancient tribe? Was it a welcome, or a warning? It looks as though it has never known a saddle. No one alive can tell why this un-penned charger yearns forever across the hill meadow, its white flanks flashing in the dawn.

Not far from where the giant chalk horse races free is the old Ridgeway, an ancient peddler's track. Along this road flints, beads and ores were lugged to the four corners of these islands. The busy trade of prehistory. A stiff westerly tramp down this path brings you to a stand of hunched trees that confide around some standing sentry sarsens. At the heart of the stone grouping is a narrow passage and a dark chamber.

Come to this place at first light. Come when the dew glimmers on a web, like a harp newly strung across the brambles and an Orb Weaver spider glowering, like a piece of amber at its centre. At this early hour the chamber is as cold as a spent hearth. It swallows the eye in its blackness. Yet listen; 'Chink, chink.' Is that a Stone Chat in the branches, or a silver buckle being hammered? Is the 'Tap, tap' a Great Tit calling, or the last touches of an iron hinge being fashioned?

Stare under the stone lintel. You know the place is empty. Nothing stirs there; only the wind that comes blustering through the bare thorns to rasp on the silent rocks. But if you came at another time, say at night, in the first cold snap of winter, when every bush crouches; then you might find the place lit and ringing.

Look now, with the eyes of just such a rambler, who has walked in curiosity up to the ring of trees and limestone passage. Now the chamber is lit and ringing. It pulses with fire. There is an immense pounding of metal on metal. Sparks fleck the darkness and there is a steady cold hiss, like a dragon's curse. For this is a smithy and Wayland toils here.

Step closer. The forge gushes yellow flames. Coals growl as an immense man stoops and pumps leather bellows. They suck at a brazier and call the coals to growl as red as Odin's eye. Who is he, this Wayland? The old Saxons knew him, as did their cousins the Germans. Wiolunt, the Rhineland Suebi called him. To the Vikings he was Volundr. The names carry something of a boar's grunt. Something of the straining arm. Wayland, means 'Battle-Brave' in the old language. But who is he, this giant smith, cauled in sweat and soot?

In his hand is a hammer, as heavy as a dead star. Yet he swings it high and down, again and again, tamping and pealing, iron on iron. His head is still. He is sandy bearded and steady. He wears a bull hide apron and a gold ring flashes in his ear. His blue eye is screwed on the point of his hammer's target and he never misses. It is hard to fathom how such a large man can work in the cramped chamber, but work he does, night after night, year after year, century after century.

With an oath he turns. In his left hand is a pair of black tongs. They hold a long sliver of steel. Its red anger is quickly fading. Wayland plunges the tongs into a trough. The water retches and seethes. He draws the waved blade from the trough and holds it to the light of his brazier. Now the steel ripples with blue. Stories and charms seem to be swimming along the sword. A weapon wrought with whispers and spells. Let me tell you, Wayland is the smith of the gods.

See how he takes a cloth and burnishes the shimmer and tang. Ten, twenty, thirty times the metal has been heated, beaten and folded back on itself. Now its edge could shear the wind. See how the smith shifts his weight and limps around the anvil. Old king Nithad did that. His men caught Wayland sleeping. They took him to an island and there they hamstrung him – cut his left leg, through the sinew, to the bone. They lamed him forever. King Nithad set him to work, and since this is all Wayland knows, work he did.

He forged plates and rings, daggers and clasps. Iron, silver, gold and tin. Wayland is the cunning master of all metals. Nithad gloated over his growing stash, fingering the pile of cups and bangles, the bright-eyed brooches. The king laughed at his good fortune and all his henchmen laughed too.

One night Nithad called for his sons, so that they too could relish all his fresh-cast wealth, and rejoice in the spectacle of the captive smith toiling through the night. The henchmen returned to the king's throne and told him his sons were nowhere to be found. High and low they had looked. Next Nithad called for his flaxen haired daughter Bodvild. Wayland had only yesterday made her an exquisite ring. The mead wenches looked for her, but she too was absent. The king shrugged and went back to his hoard. He turned the objects over in slide and clatter. His henchmen sat and drank, but one of them, looking over the rim of his cup saw Nithad's eyes widen as he poured Wayland's wares through his fingers.

For in the instant of a fire lick on the gold and silver baubles a glamour was lifted, and Nithad saw blood. Here a garnet-encrusted brooch was in fact made of fresh drawn teeth. The sapphire and emerald necklace was a link of plucked eyes. The ruby-studded goblets were wrought from skulls. The skulls of all his sons.

Nithad threw the treasure down in horror. Hoarsely he called for his men. They raced from the hall to the island where Wayland was held, but all they found was Bodvild, drugged, asleep and disordered. The beautiful diamond ring that Wayland had made for her had broken, so she took it back to him for repair. In the forge the smith had wiled with her. He gave her a sleeping potion and in his dreadful revenge Wayland had lain with the princess. As the king stood before her he saw a copper beaker, set with garnets lying dented at her side. He wept and dropped to his knees. The henchmen ran amok, clattering over tongs, pokers, bellows. They searched every corner and nook, but there was no trace of the smith. No trace at all; until one of them looked up the chimney and saw Wayland small in the sky. He had forged cool eagle's wings from moon silver and now he was beating away along a tail of stars to the west.

There are no legends to tell when Wayland set his Smithy up among the stones near Uffington. When the English came they found him here striking blades and stoking his brazier. He seems bound by obligations beyond human ken. And this is probably a good thing, considering how grim and vengeful he can be when wronged. No one has ever heard his voice. Only in the working of metal do his thoughts flow. Instead of words his language is the intricate snakes on a chieftain's shield, whirling storm-crows on a cauldron's lip.

Many have come to Wayland with their commissions, and some he has accepted. Beowulf, the great warrior had him make a close fitting mail shirt that proved secure and fast, even against the clutches of the demon Grendel. Charlemagne and Roland both carried keen, ringing swords that were tuned on Wayland's anvil.

In the 1940's they dug a barrow at Sutton Hoo and found the grave of Raedwald, king of the East Angles. Chiefest of all the treasures they pulled from the ground is a helmet, masked and paneled with many engravings. The earth had eaten much of the metal, but when it was new it would have gleamed. There are some who say that only Wayland could have made such a helm, with its nose piece, dragons and cunning inlays.

Fire crawls on his wrist guard. He stands in the ruddy light. The clang and patter are ceaseless. It would be best to draw away now, carefully in the darkness, so as not to snap a twig, or stir the leaves. It would not be a good idea to break the concentration of the smith.

And so he toils, away from the concerns of men, working his doom through iron and gold, for unknown clients. Yet, local people say if you tether your horse (preferably a white one) to the wind-bitten ash tree near the passage and chamber, and if you leave some coins on a flat stone, then your horse will be shod by morning with shoes the weight and lustre of little crescent moons. When you mount at sunrise and ride towards the chalk carving at Uffington, your horse will fly across the downland, as if it has never known a saddle, its hooves scarcely touching the dew, its white flanks flashing in the dawn.

The White Stag

C ome October my father would get the urge for musty woodland. On Sundays he would shake us gently from sleep while it was still dark. Before even the birds had woken his blue Cortina chugged outside our tidy council house and under a big windy sky we left the estate for the drive towards the wide forest that runs all the way from Patching to Burpham.

Today I speak of one such break of day trip. It is a memory that glistens like a stone under fast sluice water. See, I can reach in and fetch it now, weighing it in my hand for a while before it dries and dulls. Then I place it back in the running leet of years, where straightaway it takes its shine again.

Warren, my brother, sits in the back of the car. I am sixteen years old and he is nine. It is only a month since my grandfather died and I think of him as we pass Blessed Martyrs Church that he helped to build. Warren is still wearing his pyjama top. His dark eyes watch in the gloom. We leave the dual carriageway. The tail scuts of just woken rabbits dash away from our headlights. We park on the deep grass verge where the trees thicken on Blakehurst Lane. We have entered the marches where the delved and built on land falters, and the woodland leads up to the Downs.

My father walks ahead. His 1970's hair has grown long around his collar in tawny curls. In his mouth is a red-lit fag. He strides through a gap between two pillars of bramble. It is the thriving time of the day. We walk into a net of thrush and blackbird chatter. All is busy and creaking in the thorns and hedges. We have come for the pale, night-grown flesh of the horse mushrooms that rise in lonely paddocks when no one is looking; fairy rings, set like little gravestones among the wet nettles. Taste them raw at six o'clock on a Sunday morning and your mouth fills with the earthy sighs of old trees. In October, before the frosts and after the blossoms, there is nothing white in the woods, so the mushrooms are easy to spot.

Further in there is a bank my father knows only, where the penny buns nub through the leaves and the oaks have fallen and then grown sideways long over the bank. He leads us and we trail like one of those scenes painted on a Russian lacquered box, where three hunters, each one smaller than the other are spied on by silver badgers and foxes, who twist unseen around every root. In our case the green and gold woods indeed appear deserted. My brother looks upwards. His nut-brown face is turned up to the flitter gossip of starlings in the branches. My father blows smoke and is silent. I huddle in my coat.

Now as I look back thirty-five years I pour myself into my younger vessel and see with his eyes, think with his thoughts. I am surprised by how cool and placid and empty my young mind is on this chilly morning. Our family are early risers and even in the pulse of my surly teenage I have accepted the waking and summons to walk the autumn glades without rancour. We move through ash stump coppices. Cut down and sprung again, they are among the oldest trees. Some of them have shivered through eight hundred winters. Here each of us takes up a stick to swish and poke and tap. This is a rule of the forage. A new green stick for each visit, to be cast away again when we return to the car. Hazel, beech and laurel, the woods soon fold around us. Our feet shush the leaves which are a faded rumour of the green summer.

The bank my father only knows is in a place where the forest floor is all folded and buckled, as if trenches were dug here long ago. And there are stones, the relics of walls, and deep cratered charcoal pits all clutched and torn with roots. It is odd to stand on this bank. We lean forward as if we are riding the tilting deck of a galleon. The rising light fingers sideways across our faces and the wind blusters like a breaking wave. All is sway and buck around us. There is a pheasant feather among the oak litter. It scoots over when it is caught by the breeze and its tiger bars flicker in the shafts of morning. We look up along the bank, prodding here and there in the earth. There do not appear to be any mushrooms here today. When we have mooched the soil we straighten. Our hair flutters in our eyes.

The wind drops suddenly to a hush on my cheek as it switches tack, to blow in now from the direction of the dawn. We turn to the sudden sound of branches snapping in the distance and a pause comes in the trees as all the birds hold their voices. We stand low on the bank, my father, me and my brother, like three pegs of diminishing size hammered into the soil.

Then we see him come weaving through the trees, on the blade of a new easterly wind, as white and cool as a funeral lily. The pale stag of the morning is ghost white and clean, his head thrown back with the weight of his wide antlers. His mouth is open and his breath comes in white clouds. Then he is above us on the top of the bank, and his flank is cleanly white like a new altar cloth in the moments before the mass. The dazzle of his white-ness is almost gone before he has come, so I am still seeing the flash of him approaching us as he kicks away from us. It seems as if he holds the rising sun in the thicket of his branched tines. He is strong and dark eyed and white, and fixed in my eyes as if he is painted in a medieval bestiary which has been snapped by a 1970's Polaroid camera. We three watch silently as he passes down through the oaks towards the west.

What would my phlegmatic grandfather, who had so recently gone his way, have thought to have seen the white stag in the morning? He would know him certainly for a messenger sent to the world. And despite his lack of education would be able to tell us something of the sacred nature of the pure white beast. Never to be slain. Never to be hunted. It could never be captured. A holy breeze of an animal like a white sheet whicked away from your body. As white as a wish on a Sunday. Did not St Patrick turn himself into a white deer to pass unnoticed before the soldiers of the wicked king O'Leary? And wasn't the great Oisin named the 'young fawn' because his mother had been transformed into a deer by the druid Fir Diorich. King Arthur and his knights followed the white stag who beckoned them through secret ways and left them horseless and confused one miserable sunrise.

What would my grandfather have said of this downwind stag?

A working man, who had left school at seven years old, he would tell us such hints of these things that he knew. But my Grandfather was not there…

And neither was I.

For many years I had carried a triptych in my mind of that encounter, portable and ready to be placed on whatever sill, wherever I found myself to be resting. This three paneled memory, opened with my brother and I on one side, and my father on the other. On the centre panel the miraculous white stag came slantwise down towards us, about his own business, with scarcely a look in our direction. In far-off Galicia and in Ireland, in ratty London digs I had intoned the memory, as a precious personal relic.

However, in the weeks after my mother died, there were many nights when we three consoled ourselves in drink and such reminiscences that might make us smile. Mostly, for our father, we gleaned our shared past for tales of wonder or humour that would perhaps give him pleasure for a passing moment in the numb-sundered darkness of his loss. One such evening, when our heads were bent together over a table of many empty glasses, I laid before my brother and my father the flash of the white stag coursing through the trees as we stood like rustic peasants on the bank deep in the autumn woods. I was astonished at their laughter. I was never there, they said. It was just the two of them. I protested. I argued, for the opened triptych blazed with certainty in my eyes. Until at last my brother slammed the panels shut with the sudden confounding proof that I had been away in France that sharp morning of the white stag. And Warren had not been wearing his pyjamas.

So how then am I to proceed with this? I can see the vision of the white stag still. It is my memory and I cannot wipe it away. I turn my head from this page and the tableaux is framed on the blank wall. There is my brother, small and brown in his pyjama top and my father, younger than I am now, with his dull golden curls, and all three of us are standing in a dumbfounded row before the white Forest Lord. I know that it is impossible, this keepsake of mine. Impossible that it should live in my head. Yet, this borrowed and never-was-for-me vision is clear and alive and mine, and it will go with me until my last day.

Now my father lies clawed in his bed and all his memories have been torn into scraps that flitter up untethered and out of sequence to his grey eyes. Yet the dementia has gentled him. He dwells contentedly in the continuous present of his past. My sister has been in her grave for eleven years but she still drops by to see him in the morning, he says. All the dead talk to him. Now he is working on the building sites in London. He is a boy again. He is a young father, making a doll's house one Christmas eve fifty years ago. His mother sits with him sometimes although no one can see the pale shade of her, nor the comfort she gives. He is given to gnomic and wry utterances. Clear sentences that trail away into fathoms where we cannot go.

Perhaps many of our original myths were learned from old people whose castaway minds wandered the borders between two dimensions. Occasionally when I stand over my father and look into his eyes I know that he is not seeing me. At these times I often wonder if the white stag is in there. Does he watch it come cresting through the trees on a bright morning. Lying in his care home bed, does he still catch sight of the broad antlers in the trees, framed perhaps between pictures of my brother and I at school, as babies or as the men we are now in middle age.

One day soon I am sure the stag will come to him, as white as a banner of truce between this and the other world. My father will rise from his rumpled bed and follow the white stag that can never be caught. It will lead him ever inwards and westwards, on and on, to the greenest heart of the forest.

The Selkie

October is dying quickly now. They bring me soup but I have no appetite. My skin is the colour of a dull, stale lemon. The door to my room is always open. I can sometimes hear the other people turn and shift in their beds. The doors of the red buses hiss in the street below. My limbs are not much more than a bundle of tent poles. I can see the tops of North London trees and beyond them the milky evening. When I am awake I think again and again of last year. When I sleep, I dream of white shells on a dazzlingly fresh beach.

It was one of the last of the long days. An island in the Outer Hebrides where the water and sun drew my eyes out beyond all notions of distance. I had been following the coastal path, climbing the rocks and dunes, with the wind always in my face. It baffled ceaselessly like a light-bending banner, so that by mid-afternoon I felt as clean and cold as a sea-stripped shell. I had seen nobody.

About four in the afternoon I came to a long white strand bordered on either side by jaws of black rocks stretching out into the surf. I stood on the sand and watched the outward draw of the waves as they turned their backs to the land. It was at this moment that I felt London and the south had at last been plucked and flung away - at least for a few days. The recent divorce, at times angry, but mostly numb and sad, had eclipsed everything. I had come north to walk and to wash my thoughts out. I sat down between two skeins of flotsam and put my knees under my chin. Gulls sliced across the blue sky. There were starfish, limpets and razor-clams at my feet.

Gradually the cold got inside my rustling jacket. I looked at my map and saw that the hotel was only about a mile distant. The sand pulled at my ankles as I climbed up to the path. Cresting the dune made me breathless. I realised I was tired. The wind was endless like fishing lines being paid out over my shoulders, however a sharp scolding snap cut through it all and instinctively I turned my head. All I could see were ripples of the wind across tall grass, all the way up to the blue mountains. Snap, the sound came again. At the report of it the gulls banked away, mewling into the sun. Once more I turned towards the sound. The tall grass parted and now I saw the walls of a small house. It was down in a shallow hollow. The sound came a third time and I realised that it was a door slamming against the jam. And now I heard the creak as it opened again on the tail of the wind.

Now I had seen quite a few of the old blackhouses on my walk. I'd read all about them. One source had described them as 'the most primitive of all North Atlantic dwellings.' I have heard that on other islands in the Hebrides people have restored some the blackhouses as holiday homes but all I had seen on this island were in ruins. Yet from where I stood, I could see that the chimney was still intact, and there was also obviously a door. It lay off the path, across the tousled grass. It took me about six minutes of wading the grassy tide to get close.

I came up to it at the gable end. It was a tiny structure. The chimney was scarcely higher than my head. I walked around the right hand side and saw the low doorway. It was like the house a child might draw when thinking of the dark fairies, or a witch. I now saw straightaway that this dwelling was also long gone to disorder. At some time someone had patched the turf roof with sheets of corrugated iron, but some of these had sheared off, and lay twisted in the grass. The one window was glassless.

I watched the door swing out. It was made of four planks. They were split and eaten at the bottom like a set of broken teeth. The seesaw wind pulled it away on its rusty hinges and then pushed it

70

back. This house must have been inhabited far later than the others on the island; there were still flakes of green paint on the door.

The door swung out again but more slowly, for the wind had dropped a little. Moss had greened the dark stones. There was a sort of rough path up to the door, which I now saw sloped away in the direction of the beach. I guessed that sheep might huddle in the house on cold nights. I was stilled for a while in thoughts of transience and decay when I glimpsed flashes of white on the floor, just across the threshold. There in the gloom I saw three garlands of flowers. I bent slightly, still holding the door, but the muscle of the wind was strong and it was hard to wrestle against it. Clumsily I reached out into the gloom and grasped one of the garlands. To my surprise it was sharp, like clutching shards of porcelain. Stepping back, I let the door go and it slammed furiously. This time even the returning wind could not budge it. I looked down at my hand. It was indeed a garland, but one made of seashells. White cockles, augers and dog whelks all strung together. They clinked dry and hollow between my fingers. There had been three of these on the floor of the blackhouse. What naïve, votive fancy, I wondered, had bought them here? I imagined a young girl placing them and then running back to her parents down on the sand. The garland, or bracelet, was the sort of thing I would have once saved to take home for my wife, but that was all done now. Nevertheless, I placed it in the pocket of my anorak, to lie alongside a two mallard feathers and a piece of sea glass I had collected on my walk.

I went back down the sheep path to the beach. In the few minutes I had been poking around the blackhouse the balance of the day had tipped towards evening. For all the wicking and insulation of modern walking clothes, I began to shiver a little as I walked the last mile. The wind died away completely as I rounded the headland. There was the harbour and early lights in the windows of the houses. The sea was now calmer than it had been all day. I looked out and saw the bobbing heads of two or three seals. It was hard to tell exactly, for they dipped and surfaced at irregular intervals. They subjected me to a large-eyed and silent scrutiny. Watchful sea-dogs; seals always seem to have time just to linger and stare, safe in their chilly water.

I went back through to the bar after dinner. I had eaten fish pie. The waitress was a nimble, polite and serious Lithuanian. She didn't want to talk much. The only other diners were a monotone Dutch couple in nautical clothes and their glum son who chased his scampi around the plate but didn't eat it. The waitress seemed to want us to leave. She said that the kitchen closed at eight thirty, it being the end of the season. The Dutch family paid and went back to their yacht. I thought a single malt or two might do me good. The waitress clicked the lights off as soon as I left the room.

I opened my guide book and some postcards I had bought the night before fell out. As I sat up on the barstool I wondered who on earth would wish to receive them. My daughter was off travelling somewhere in New Zealand. My ex-wife had gone off to live in Cornwall. I had bought a flat with my share of the equity. Colleagues at the school never referred to my divorce. Never invited me to dinner either. Walking at least was something I could do alone with no fear of being singled out as odd. The very act of striking out across the landscape zipped into man-made fibres makes you an acceptable loner. I put the postcards away.

The bar was empty. I reached across and rang the bell. I could hear a television in the back room. I had taken my jacket down with me to dinner, with view to a walk along the harbour wall before the last of the sunset. I hung it on a hook by my knee. Three yachts were moored there. The light had not quite gone, and there were flecks of rain on the window. The door behind the bar opened. The landlord Mr Bisset had a swallow tattooed on each hand; obviously an ex-naval man. When I remarked on this he pointed to a photo of himself in his chief petty officer's uniform. He had bought Taigh Na Mara eleven years ago, he told me, as he filled my glass. He had the palest blue eyes and a mild Highland accent.

'Our retirement,' said Mr Bisset as he straightened the bar tow-

72

el. He gave me a small jug of water for the whisky. 'When we took over it was really run down. We spent a year fixing it up.'

'Wonderful location,' I replied, raising my glass to him. 'Cheers.'

'Slainte,' he said, quickly and almost without expression.

I sipped the whisky. 'That's good,' I said.

Mr Bisset nodded, looking out at the harbour. 'Rain coming in,' he said. 'It'll be a mixed day tomorrow.'

'I don't mind the rain. At least, not up here. It kind of washes one's hopes clean. It's different in London.'

'Is that so?' Now he looked at me with a chief petty officer's stare. Clearly Mr Bisset was not a romantic.

'The fish pie was excellent,' I said, after floundering for a second.

'Aye, Shona does that well. Anything with fish. Desserts too. I couldn't run the kitchen without her.' He seemed to be half listening to the TV in the back room. I could hear snatches of Gaelic. It sounded like a chat show. 'Mind you, we're quiet now,' he added.

'I suppose it takes a strong marriage to run a business like this.'

'Shona's not my wife,' snapped Mr Bisset. 'She lives along the road and comes in for the cooking. My wife died six years ago.'

'Oh I'm sorry.' I seemed to be making a blunder of everything that came out of my mouth.

'No bother. You weren't to know.' Then he smiled slightly. 'Retirement.' He said. 'You think you've got everything planned, but you can never tell.' I nodded, agreeing silently that he was right on that score. 'Another one?' he asked, looking at my nearly empty glass.

'Yes please.' I shifted and felt the tiredness in my legs. It would not be long until I was for my bed. Mr Bisset poured the drink. It was the only sound apart from the ticking of a battered longcase clock in the corner. I searched for something to say. I remembered the shells in my jacket pocket.

'Here,' I said. 'Look what I found on my way here today.' I laid them on the bar.

Mr Bisset had refilled the little water jug and he paused slightly before putting it down.

'Shells?' He asked.

'Yes, but all strung together. See?' I touched the point on one of the spiralled augers.

'Where did you get them?'

'On the floor of one of the ruined houses. There were two others like this.'

'We've a great many shells here on the island.' Mr Bisset's head was again inclined towards the back room and his television programme.

'Yes but I thought it curious that they were strung together like this and placed on the floor. I wondered if it was a children's folk custom or something'

'We've a great many shells,' he repeated. I could see that it did not interest him at all.

'If you want anything else just ring the bell.'

With that he left me in the bar alone. I was a little stung by the way he had brought the shutters down on our conversation. I drew my last whisky out for about twenty minutes. No one else came in. I sat alone looking out at the dark sea and the rain flecking more thickly against the window. Too wet for a walk, so at last I went up, taking the garland of shells with me.

A storm rose after midnight. I woke as it rattled at the roof and the gable. There were lulls and blasts. Occasionally the gale died away completely for a while and in those pauses only a low moaning filled the darkness and a curious chink chink sound like ice cubes being dropped into a glass. In one of these respites I got up and went to the window. It was all drenched darkness out there. The chinking continued and underneath it the soft mournful moan. My window was smudged. I sat on the deep sill and rubbed it away. There was the white hull of the Dutch family's yacht bobbing in the harbour. I could see the moon through its rigging. Nothing else moved apart from the water. Chink chink. I realised that the sound was the slap of the metal halyards, for as the gust came again the sound grew more urgent, like the tapping of a toffee hammer. The moaning was again quickly stifled. I imagined it must also come from the wind vibrating in the rigging.

I went back to bed and must have fallen into half sleep for I dreamed I heard the knock on my bedroom door before it actually happened. I had probably heard the footsteps along the corridor. I sat up 'Hello?' I coughed for inflection in my voice was more high pitched than I intended.

'It's me...Bisset. Can I have a word?' I rose and felt an odd dreary tiredness, realising that I had not been as awake as I had thought. I slipped into my jeans. Mr Bisset was standing in the hall with a bottle and two glasses in his hands.

I sat on the deep will of the window. Mr Bisset was in the cane chair. He looked at the floor and rubbed the stubble of his chin. I must have had a rather tousled and confused expression but as he seemed to be struggling for words I too remained silent. I watched as he poured two drams. When at last he spoke, his voice was hoarse.

'I owe you an apology.'

'What for? And why at this hour?'

He took a sip. He was sat in the lemon glare of the tall standard lamp over his shoulder. 'I was abrupt with you this evening . . . more than I should have been.'

'And you've come here with whisky to apologise for that? Do you rouse all your guests in the early hours like this?'

'There are no other guests,' he said. Again there was a note of irritation. I wondered how much he had been drinking. But then his tone softened. 'Give me a minute' he said. 'This isn't easy.'

'Don't worry' I swirled the dram in my glass. 'I was awake anyway. The storm...'

He interrupted me, 'I know water. I have ridden the decks of frigates through five-day squalls above Iceland. I've seen days of sunlight and calm off Shetland when the sea buckles slowly and flexes like an oiled muscle. Black and white and green as glass, I've seen it. Many times as we were cruising home in the Channel I looked at weed suspended two fathoms down and felt my eye drawn to the deep.' He paused, looking down at his knees.

75

'You're certainly, more poetic than first impressions would suggest,' I said. 'However, I don't see the pressing need to give me your thoughts on the sea.'

He held his hand up. 'Please,' he said. 'I can only tell it this way.'

'Very well. Like I tried to say to you - I can't sleep with all the knocking outside and that groaning sound, whatever it is. Go ahead. I'll sit and be quiet until you have finished.'

'Thanks,' he replied.

He seemed genuinely relieved with my permission, but I felt I was bound to listen to him whether I liked it or not. Nevertheless, he sat back more easily in the cane chair.

'I was twenty five years in Navy. Joined at seventeen; there was nothing but fishing here when I was a boy and now there isn't even much of that. Or at least not enough to make a living. Anyway, I went to sea. It's all our family have ever done, one way or another.

Now there was a great uncle of mine, Tom MacPhail. He fished alone, for his two older brothers were killed in 1916 at Jutland. Tom was my mother's brother. I never knew him. It was his cabin you were at today, or what remains of it.' He paused and took another sip of his whisky. 'My mother was very much younger than Tom, but even so she came from a world before television and films. The island was all Gaelic speaking then and folk would sit at night telling the old stories. What happened to my great uncle Tom MacPhail was part of an old world that is almost gone now. I had the story form my mother many times and took it to my heart, so I can tell it to you now as if she was whispering it in my ear.

He was a quiet young man and kept himself to himself. It may be a mile and half to his house but it could have been a hundred for all any one saw of him. He took the death of his bothers hard. My mother and my grandparents lived away near the manse on the other side of the island. Tom MacPhail had grey eyes. He wore a blue ganzie and simple cuaran shoes. His trousers were patched and patched over again. He only came to the harbour

76

when he had a good catch and that was rarely. The only time he bothered anyone was when he needed a stack of turf.

Tom knew the sea better than any of us. He knew its cunning and its treachery. He knew its gentle shift when the bright sunlight breaks on the waves and nearly blinds you. He knew that feeling of being watched when you are out there on quiet water. For years he slept alone in the wee blackhouse, eating his fried mackerel and oat cakes. Even in those days the island was half empty. Many had gone to Canada or Glasgow. There were few single girls. As soon as they came of age most just wanted to fly away. My mother thought that Tom had put marriage out of his mind altogether - after all, he had little to offer a wife. He mended his nets and sat on the sand and watched the big clouds break on the mountains.

His house was just one room. It contained a bed, a stove, an iron chest and a table. As I understand it, one particular night he was sitting and reading a week old newspaper by the light of his oil lamp. This would be in 1929. It was about this time of year. Tom looked up, for he had heard a sound outside. It was laughter. A girl's laughter. Laughter like sunny seawater being poured from a pail. I have said that Tom was a quiet man. He never rushed. But he frowned at the sound of that laughter and went to the door. He opened it slowly. The strand was all silver in the moonlight. He walked out under the stars, cocking his head. Nothing. Nothing, save the quiet waves stroking the shells and making them chuckle at low tide. Now a man can hear many things in the voice of the sea and Tom began to think that he had been mistaken. There had been no laughter, he thought. Perhaps it was a woken curlew? He put his hand through his fair hair and looked along the whole length of the strand.

Then he saw her. Silver in the moonlight, she knelt by a pool at the far end where the rocks rise from the sand. Tom walked in silence. She knelt with her back to him. He heard her laugh again, and it was glad, like herring flashing in a creel. She was naked and as white as the breast of a gull. Tom went towards her with a strange trembling in his chest. He was nearly standing over her when she heard his footfall in the sand. With a thin cry of terror she leapt up and away from him. In that instant Tom saw that she had been watching two crabs duelling in the moonlight. He glimpsed the cool white of her limbs and her breasts, her up-turned nose and black eyes. Her long hair was flung like oarweed away from her face. Dark also was the bundle she snatched up as she made to run. Yet Tom had taken hold of it as well. For a second they both pulled against each other but Tom was the stronger. With a look of wild panic her fingers slipped from the bundle and she ran away over the rocks to the water. Tom tried to follow her but she was nimble and had disappeared into the crags and crevices. He slipped on a sharp black edge and cut his knee. He called after her but she had been swallowed by the night. He was left breathless and amazed at what had just happened.

He looked down at the soft garment. He had no idea why he had held onto it. It was all tinged with moon-silver. It was the pelt of a grey seal. Confused and stung with astonishment he walked back past his boat to his wee house. There by the light of the oil lamp he studied the pelt. Here were the two eye holes; here the mottled brown and black spots. He ran his hands over the soft fur. Tom was by no means slow-witted but the reckoning of what he had in his hands took a while to come to him. Nevertheless, sitting at his table he recalled old stories that the islanders told throughout the generations. He sat there musing for a while then he reached down the collar of his blue ganzie. Around his neck was a leather thong on which hung a black iron key. Tom took the key and opened the chest which lay under his bed. This chest held what little money he had. Carefully he folded the sealskin and placed it in the chest. Then he poured a dram to steady himself and sat back down with his eyes on the door.

Around the time when the wind changed direction and Tom's head was drooping to his chest there came a knock. The oil lamp was guttering low. He got up and opened the door. There against

78

the night stood the young woman. She was naked and whiter than new linen. Her hair glistened darkly like sea coal. Tom took the woman's hand and led her into his wee house. He told her that he wanted her to be his wife. He told her that he had her seal pelt locked in his iron chest. For a while she said nothing but the look on her face was as bleak and sad as a January morning. From her dark, dark eyes came a chain of slow tears. At last she spoke and her voice was indeed like a curlew. Her wild words made the hairs on Tom's arms tingle.

'Fisherman,' she said. 'You know that I know that you have what is most precious to me. You know that I know that I cannot go back to the sea without it.' The young woman breathed in and the hooks of her tears caught in her throat. She looked down to where her bare white feet stood on the rushes of Tom's floor. 'Yet I know that you know that I am bound to obey you.'

Tom MacPhail smiled. He told her that he would treat her well and that in time she would grow to love him. But the woman from the sea held up her hand. 'Fisherman,' she said.

'Many times I have looked up in cool green water and seen you draw in your nets. I have seen your face swimming in the air as you leaned out from your boat. I do not think I can love you. Your people are not favourable to me.'

'Be that as it may,' he said, 'You will be my bride.'

'For all of seven years,' she replied. 'And then you know that I know that you must set me free.' Tom nodded, realising that a solemn doom had settled between them.

The face of the woman from the sea was white and beautiful as midnight snow, but the wrack of sadness was ever in her eyes. Tom MacPhail did his best to make her happy. He ordered a dress for her from the mainland. He gave her a mirror and a comb of ivory. Shoes she would never wear. She learned to cook fish for him, for she had always eaten them raw. The turf fire was a new and absorbing object of fascination. She spent hours stoking it and watching the low flames. Yet she was always drawn away from the house to the shore. Sometimes Tom would stand in his doorway as she wandered the length of the strand in the rain. Her gaze was ever for the place nine waves out and Tom often saw seals there watching his wife. When she returned she would stand drenched and dripping on the rushes. She spoke little and of her life in the sea she would not speak at all, saying he would not understand. She would not come out in his boat.

When he stripped to wash he sometimes caught her looking at the black key he wore around his neck, but Tom knew that iron had a binding power over her kind. And so he also slept easy, never fearing that she would take the key at night.

The two of them lived in near silence, away from other people. No one knew that Tom MacPhail had taken a sea woman for a wife. After a year her belly swelled. She went out to the rock pool one spring night and returned with a baby son. She wrapped him in seaweed and gave him sprats to eat. After another year her belly swelled again and she brought a baby girl home. She fed her shrimps. The two children were as quiet as their mother. They sat on the sand and played with white cockles.

The seasons came and went. The children grew. Tom became less and less successful with the fishing, for the seals out in the bay would often tear his nets. So his wife foraged for mussels and razor clams and stewed them for their supper. Every time he looked at the woman from the sea desire swam up inside him, but at night when oil lamp glowed over his family Tom found himself reflecting that his marriage had not brought him contentment. True that as time passed his wife's affection for him had grown. She kept the wee house clean and washed his shirts. She sometimes smiled when he bought her flowers, or a piece of sea glass. Yet once or twice he had found his wife and children out near the rock pool laughing their high curlew laughter, watching together as two crabs duelled in the clear water. They never laughed that way with him. But Tom, being a steady man, of quiet disposition bore his sadness without comment.

However, it was a shock when one day his wife came to stand before him in the light of the morning with her hands on her hips.

'Fisherman,' she said. 'I have lain beside you for many nights. I have given you a son and a daughter. I have sewn your clothes. But now seven years has passed and I must take my freedom.' She was framed in the doorway and as beautiful as if she had been crowned with white hawthorn.

'Haven't we made a life here on the strand?' Tom asked.

'I was only bound to you for seven years,' she replied. 'And now I must go back to the water. You know it.'

Suddenly it was as though Tom's limbs were being pulled by unseen hands or that he was merely a string puppet, for he felt himself walk towards the chest and take the key from below his blue ganzie. He saw his hands unlock and open the chest. And then he lifted out the lustrous pelt that had been folded away for seven years.

The woman from the sea took her sealskin from him. 'Do not think that this is easy fisherman. You were good to me. We twined ourselves. But you tied me to the land and I was always looking forward to the day when I could go to my people.' Tears stood in her dark eyes like pearls. She turned and walked out of the wee house. And that was the last Tom MacPhail ever saw of his wife.'

Mr Bisset looked at me. He cleared his throat and looked down at his knees, as if he was embarrassed by the quiet space between us now that his story was finished.

'Am I supposed to be searching for some kind of allegory in what you have just told me?' I asked.

'I don't know what you mean,' he replied.

'You have a gift for storytelling, but I must admit to being completely baffled as to why you have spent the last twenty minutes giving me a wonderful account of your uncle and his mermaid wife'

'No, not a mermaid,' he said.

'Whatever,' I snapped. 'I'm weary. Sleepless night and hotel owner pouring me whisky and relating fables in the early hours. This will look great on Tripadvisor.'

'It's the shells' he said. 'That's why I wanted to explain what happened.'

'The shells?'

'Aye, let me see them again.' I went and took them from my coat pocket. Mr Bisset held out his hand. 'Were there more?'

'Yes, three in total.' He nodded and frowned as he ran his fingers over them.

'Look Mr Bisset I...' But he interrupted me. 'You need to take them back,' he said. 'What on earth for? Have I really stumbled on some folk custom?' He shook his head. 'You need to take them back.' Again he gave me his chief petty officer's stare.

'When?'

'Now.'

'Can it not wait until the morning?'

He looked past me up at the window. 'It is the morning. Do you not hear the wind changing? No? Well it doesn't matter.' He repeated it a third time, 'You need to take them back.'

The rain had stopped. We walked along the road until it gave out onto the footpath. Mr Bisset was in front. I had that slightly sick and keen feeling of being out before the dawn. It was still dark but there was a creeping grey promise of light on the horizon. My bones resented every step but I was curious, given what Mr Bisset had told me as we prepared to leave the hotel.

'It is impossible to keep a wild woman,' he said as searched for his keys. 'Tom MacPhail learned that.'

'Are you asking me to believe that his wife actually came out of the sea?'

'I don't care what you believe.'

'What happened to him?'

Mr Bisset opened the front door. His voice fell to a whisper in the fresh black air. 'He carried on living alone. People saw even less of him than before.'

'But he had the two children.' I said as we stood on the front step zipping up our jackets.

'She took the boy and girl with her.'

'To the sea?'

'That's what he told my mother. In 1940 he sent a note to her asking her to come to him. She found him in his bed in the throes of a fever. That's when he told her the whole story. She said he took her hand and told her that he had walked on the strand every night winter and summer, looking for his wife and children. Calling for them. When my mother came to him he was just skin and bone. She wanted to fetch the doctor and have him sent to the hospital on the mainland, but he would have none of that. He just held her hand and said 'Watch for the seals,' over and over until he slipped away.'

Now we were walking the footpath up to the dunes. High wet grass licked my fingertips. After a few minutes silence I whispered back to him. 'Ok, if I understand this right, you are saying to me that there was some old island tradition of seals transforming into women.'

'Understand is a good word. I'm not asking you to believe it, just to understand it,' he replied. 'And yes, there are stories. There are some families who claim that they are descended from the Selkies.'

'Selkies?'

'The seal people.'

'It all seems completely absurd.'

'Maybe to you,' he whispered. 'But as I said earlier, I know how wanchansy the sea can be. I've seen flotsam that looks like a face in the water. On watch at night about twenty miles off the coast of Malta myself and a young lieutenant could have sworn someone was calling both our names out in the fog. That put the chill up our necks.'

'Probably nothing but the fatigue, I should say. You and I both heard that low moaning sound when the storm was lashing the windows. You could make something weird from that if you were tired and alone.'

Mr Bisset halted and leaned his close to me. 'If I am right I think that sound could very well be something that you would call weird.'

'What the do you mean by that?' I ignored his sarcastic semblance of an English accent.

'Let's just wait and see shall we. I might be pushing this too far, so I don't want to end up looking like a fool.'

'Right now it's me who feels like the fool. I've never had a night quite like this one.' I stumbled on a stone. 'Can't believe how you talked me into coming out at this hour.'

'Ah well,' he said, 'It's not as if anyone is keeping tabs on you.'

Indeed not, I thought. Ordinarily I would not have been so easily led into this absurd tangle of myth and reminiscence. I would not have been so passive. But he was right; no one gave a damn about what I got up to anymore. And after all, this is what I had come to the Hebrides for, to cast off the settled thoughts of my daily life. At that moment that was why I was going along with Mr Bisset – for the odd pleasure of just seeing what might happen.

Soon enough we reached the dunes and we could see more now as the dawn came on. It was low tide. The sea lay quiet. The light was all grey and flat and gentle. Mr Bisset climbed up on the highest dune and cocked his head. 'Do you hear that?' he asked looking down at me. I strained my ears and heard far off the low moaning sound. I nodded to him. Together we stood looking out over the gentle waves. The more I listened I realised there were not one but two or three strands to the sound; a sonorous polyphony coming over the water.

'I was wrong,' he said at last, 'Someone is keeping tabs on you.'

'The seals?'

'Aye the seals, or whatever they are that go about in the skins of seals. They want the shells put back where they left them.' I grinned at him, feeling my wily city-self rise again, but just as quickly realised how out of place I was in this landscape and these dealings. Mr Bisset seemed aware of this, for he watched me steadily until the grin died on my face. 'Come on' he said.

The stones of Tom MacPhail's blackhouse were as cold as a

tomb. I put my hand on the windowsill and felt the chill seep into my fingers. Mr Bisset, slightly breathless, stood back and looked over the dwelling. 'I used to come here and patch it up,' he said. 'I put some new roofing on it once. Don't know why. Something for my mother, who loved him I suppose. I haven't been here for a good many years.'

He was silent for a while but I cut across his thoughts. 'So, what do we do? Put the shells back and then the seals will be satisfied? And then then you will be happy too? Honour restored?'

His pale eyes fixed me. 'You still don't understand, do you? This has nothing at all to do with making me happy. We're doing this for you!' Despite whispering there was force in his voice. I shook my head. 'Look man,' he continued wearily. 'I heard them calling before ever you did last night. My mother said always said that it doesn't do to vex the sea folk.'

'Why, what's going to happen if we do annoy them?' 'I don't know,' he replied, 'but it didn't work out so well for Tom MacPhail.' The moaning calls were rising behind us out in the minch. 'And I've never heard that noise before.'

'Very well,' I said. I took the shells from my pocket, then together we both strained at the door until we got it open. The one room of little house was musky and black. I laid the clinking garland back with the other two on the floor. There was no puff of smoke or dazzle of stars, but as we stood back the door slammed.

'Done?' I asked, wiping my hands on my jacket.

'I hope so. Now let's get back.'

We went back to the dunes. The chorus rose again and it was like the wind itself humming through shells, or a sea cave. Then it was gone altogether. We looked, but could not see any seals out there.

'It will be a good story to tell when I get back to London,' I said.

'Aye, say that we are all bloody lunatics up here.'

'But in all this palaver, I still don't quite understand why we had to put the shells back.'

'All I can tell you is that the old people said one must never

85

cause any grief to come to the Selkies. That's why the fishermen would never harm a seal, even when they damaged the nets. In taking the shells you disturbed them. They used to say that even to lay eyes on a Selkie in human form was terrible bad luck.'

'How bad?'

'Death,' he replied. 'A wasting death like that which came on Tom MacPhail.'

We had reached the black rocks at the end of the sand. But why, if what you say is true, why would these sea people would leave the shells there in the first place?'

'Because the sea woman loved him, after her fashion. As did her children. They are not of this world, but they are drawn to it. Drawn to us. They would be pining for the memory of him.'

The wind was in our hair as we stood by the rocks. It looked like it was going to be a fine yellow morning. Mr Bisset obviously thought the same. 'There will be more rain later but that's a good start to the day,' he said. Then he put his hand on my arm. 'I'll make you a good strong cup of tea when we get home.' He went a few steps ahead of me towards the footpath. 'And don't worry about the shells. Placing them back was an insurance policy...just in case.' Gulls coursed the new sky. His laughter seemed to make them yatter.

I took one last look back and squinted as the sun flashed quickly on wet stone and clean sand. For a second I could have sworn I saw a girl standing there by a rock pool, dark- haired, naked, and white as fresh sea foam.

'What is it?' asked Mr Bisset as he turned to see me rubbing my eyes.

'Nothing,' I replied.

Tuatha Dé Danann

*L*ong ago, before ever men came to the wet green islands of the west there was a morning of glower and grey rain. It was May 1st, the day of Bealtaine. Across the sea six black clouds hove in from the horizon, making shadows on the rocks and reefs of the shores of Ireland. In shape the clouds were like great ships with thunderous keels and dark prows. Eventually the cloud ships came to rest against a mountain. A strange and shining people disembarked. They ran down the slopes and the clouds on which they had ridden melted away. The rain ceased and the sun came.

Tall and beautiful in the pin-sharp light, they were black haired and white skinned. Their eyes were of the clearest blue. The men among them were keen and trim. The women were haughty and lovely. They called themselves the Tuatha Dé Danann – the Tribe of the Goddess Danu. As they wandered they built airy lodges near the rivers and lush pastures. In the daytime they fished and hunted. At night there was music in their halls such as no human ear has heard. They were above all masters of music; of the pipes, the fiddle and the harp. This was the golden time for the Dé Dananns, when they were at their most powerful.

But there were other tribes in Ireland who had been living in the faraway places since before years were counted. From the reedy marshes and from cold cave mouths the yellow eyed and hunched tribe of the Fir Bolg listened to the music of the Dé Dananns with bitter rage. In the moonlight they sent their chieftain, the fanged and foul Sreng, with an ultimatum that the shining newcomers should quit the shores of Ireland. Bres was a champion of the Dé Danann and he stepped forward to demand that the Fir Bolg give them half the island or defend it in battle. Sreng the Fir Bolg chief spat at the feet of Bres. He chose war.

At the pass of Balgatan the Fir Bolg fell upon the Dé Dananns, with whooping fury and jagged spears. However, the Dé Dananns formed up instantly and drew a thousand bronze swords, like the slant of autumn light on icy water. Their pipers stood out proudly beyond the ranks and commenced a shrieking war chant. Their archers let fly a shimmer of arrows, each fletched with iridescent mallard feathers. That was a bitter flock for the Fir Bolg. Within a minute hundreds of them lay dead on the moss. Then the Dé Dananns charged, shouting their battle slogans. They cut through the necks and tendons of the Fir Bolg. The Dé Danann women spun themselves into a rage, so that the Fir Bolg were dazzled by screams and spells. Within ten minutes most of the enemy had fallen. Those Fir Bolg who escaped ran all the way the Connacht. This was the first battle of Mag Tuired.

In their newly won lands the Dé Dananns rested in the shade of oak trees. But the clamour of battle had awakened another tribe. That evening there came a smash and crack of stones splitting in the peaks and crags above them. It was an angry sound that bewildered the Dé Dananns and one for which they had no name. In the morning they woke to find a new host bristling the hillsides. These were the Fomorians, the first tribe. They were giants, with manlike bodies and the heads of goats. They were armed with great clubs, and as they charged they struck the rocks before them into rubble and scree. They were a terrible band.

Again the Dé Dananns formed ranks and let fly their arrows. Scores of Fomorians fell with duck feathers at their throats. Again the pipers led the onslaught, so that although the Fomorians swung their clubs, it was as if they were striking against the wind, while all around them wailed the fierce Dé Dananns bagpipes. Through the Fomorian phalanxes passed the shining tribe, whirling and leaping. They lunged with their blinding swords, and before the giants could reckon their enemy they were hacked to the ground, one and all. This was the second battle of Mag Tuired.

For a time all was peaceful. The forests were glad with bluebells. The Dé Dananns listened to the songs they heard in rivers and branches. Their singing was like the morning courtship of birds. One day, when some of the shining tribe were standing in the shallows of a sandy bay they saw the sails of eight ships far out to sea. Then they heard voices, vital and emphatic, carrying across the water. The ships spread oars and the sailors pulled through the waves with decisive energy. These were the Milesian Gaels who had come all the way from Spain. They were the first mortal men to see the foam break on the shores of Ireland. The Dé Dananns could see with the eyes of eagles and hear with the ears of foxes. To them the voices of the mortal men was like rust being scraped off a spade. The red beards of the Milesians seemed to shout from their faces.

The Dé Dananns massed along the bay, their cloaks strung away from them on the wind. Their hair fluttered in dark pennants across their cool blue eyes. The Milesians stood up as their galleys grounded and they flashed their iron swords. One of them sprang into the surf. His hair was spiked with pine resin. This was Ith, the first mortal man to tread the sands of Ireland. He ran ashore yelling and looking about himself at the lush pastures and fine stands of trees. This was good land. His sword was like a streak of dull weather against the morning.

Most of the Dé Dananns had fallen back. They had never before seen the like of this naked warrior, with his chest all drawn in blue painted spirals. However, as Ith of the Milesians crested the dunes and stood on the tussock grass three Dé Danann kings rose to meet him. These were Mac Cuill, Mac Cecht and Mac Gréine. They threw their cloaks aside and fell on Ith. His blood drained into the sand. His dull sword was slung into the grass and lay there like a tongue of silent thunder. It was the first iron sword and the first mortal blood shed in Ireland.

The three Dé Dananns kings went back to their people, but as they walked inland their druids spoke of a new foreboding that come to their hearts, so the kings looked back over their shoulders to the sea...

Green eyes, hazel, brown and grey; now eight princes, the nephews of Ith, came ashore. The Dé Dananns did well to look back, for the fury of the Milesians was like a fire in the gorse that sends the deer fleeing crossways and skilly down the mountain. Through the pastures and glades the Milesians ran. They came in scores and then hundreds. These were men whose din went before them, roaring and chanting, and clanging their long swords against their shields.

Skirmish after skirmish desperately the Dé Dananns fought, but their bronze weapons shattered at the first strike of iron. At last they were beaten back all the way to the hill of Tara, the navel centre of Ireland. At Tara the Dé Dananns called a parley and asked for peace. The Milesians surrounded the Shining Tribe in fierce and silent ranks.

However, the Dé Dananns had voices more plangent and honey toned than their harps. They soothed the anger of the Milesians and made a gilded promise. They bid the Milesians to retire back to their boats and sail off to a distance of nine waves. Their oath was this; if the Milesians could make the shore again the Dé Dananns would surrender up the land.

Strangely quietened, and beguiled as if they had drunk too much mead, the Milesians went back their galleys. They set sail and the Dé Dananns watched them go. And when the ships reached the nine waves distance they uttered their most powerful magic and called up a storm. The ocean rose in collapsing ramparts. The eight Milesian ships bucked on the waves like loose saddles on panicked stallions. Five of the nephews of Ith were drowned. However, among the crew of one ship was the great bard Amergin. He stood up and sang a song of such sweet calm that the sea lay down suddenly like a well-trained hound.

The dismay of the shining tribe was like a sudden sickness among them, for as they looked down on the white strand the saw the three remaining nephews of Ith drag themselves from the surf. These men were Emer, Finn and Éremón. The three Dé Dananns kings Mac Cuill, Mac Cecht and Mac Gréine were called out to combat, by hard mortal voices. All three of them fell. This was the battle of Tailtiu.

From amid the grieving Dé Dananns queens and children their druids came forth to ask the bard Amergin to mediate between the two tribes. Amergin stood on the field of Tailtiu which was strewn with spring flowers and Dé Dananns corpses. At last he offered a solution. The Milesians should take a half portion of the land and the Dé Dananns should take the other. Amergin made both parties agree with binding oaths. But, too late, the Dé Dananns discovered that Amergin had tricked them. The half portion of mortal men was to be all the land above ground. The portion of the Dé Dananns was to be the land below the turf and rocks.

There was never before or since such a keening and weeping in Ireland as there was that morning when the Dé Dananns realised the truth of their fate. The host of the shining tribe passed between the ranks of the Milesian spearmen to openings in the green hills. They proceeded through craved archways into the darkness of their new home beneath the earth. Strong men then rolled great stones across the entrances and walked away, brushing off their gritty hands on their breeches. This was to be the end of the conflict. Men now commanded all the fields and forests and valleys and lochs.

Yet this was not the end of the story. Not at all.

Exactly where the Tuatha Dé Danaan went and how they fashioned their new kingdom is beyond the knowledge of mankind. It is true that they departed into the hills, but it is also certain that they do not exist in dark, earthy chambers. They took all their beauty with them and sustained their new realm wholly by magic. It is nowhere, no place, beyond time. It is true that this country can sometimes be reached through doors in the hills. Some men and women have been into the hidden kingdom. However, if they return to tell their stories it is always as if they are trying to recall a dream. Men have named the place of the Dé Dananns Tír na nÓg, or 'Land of the Ever Young.'

Yet this land of song and eternal twilight does not satisfy them. They have never forgotten their banishment and the great wrong that men did them. They foster a grudge that has worried deep into their hearts. They resent that humans may taste the wind on their faces, spring water on their lips, the sun at noon glinting on the sea. In their long years of exile these things they have not forgotten. And indeed many of them come back to the world.

The proscriptions on the liberty of the Dé Dananns are not known. The manner by which they can pass the green gates of the hollow hills is also a mystery. However, there seem to be many regulations on their freedom. For instance, they chiefly appear at the gloaming and they depart before dawn. Crossroads are a favourite haunt of theirs, as are waterfalls and mountain pools.

They frequent all wild places.

They are great riddlers and hagglers. Never, enter into a transaction with them. Do not eat their food or take their drink. They have many forms of enchantment, but chiefly they have the power to glamour the unwary and gullible. They fear all Christian trappings, and priests are anathema to them. Above all they fear iron. Crossing the threshold into our world, when the evening shadows lengthen, they come in many guises, many forms, but I will tell you the names and natures of some of them, so you can be on your guard against their wiles and dealings.

Cú Chulainn and the Morrigan

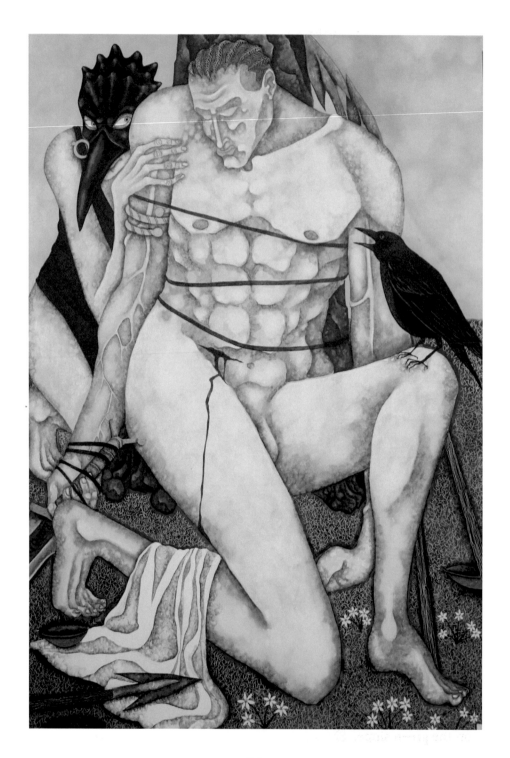

I see him through a crow's eye. He is tied to the white stone. This is where he has come to die. He holds his sword high, despite his wounds. The blade takes the flame of the setting sun. I circle high above the white pillar which is the hub of the great plain. From his feet the corpses of his enemies radiate, like the spokes of a bloody wheel. There is his smashed chariot with one black horse still kicking in the harness. I soar away into the blustery nightfall, screaming in joy at the slaughter.

What is this time you people all go by? This way you have of being in years? I am now, and now I am in your eye. Before him, before you, after all - at the end and outside the end. I come fast, swooping on black wings. I am at your ear. I am in your skull. Here, let me roost in the white bone chamber and tell you of this boy who grows to be man. Let me tell you of his thunder feats. Yet do not expect me to give the ordered seasons of his life, for this sequence I do not understand. Therefore my telling will be all out of kilter for you . . .

Like an unseen pennant I fly in the wake of a currach coming to land on a white strand. A sleek boat of pitched leather and red sails. High above are peaks where the sea eagles turn. Two boys jump from the prow into chilly surf. Here is Ferdiad running to the grass beyond the dunes, fleet-footed, black- haired, eyes full of the twist and fiddle of the wind. Here is our man with Ferdiad, but he is still a youngster yet, for his years have not risen in him. He is brown limbed and golden curled, as if the sun is laughing on his shoulders. He leaps tussocks and makes for a hut on the green slope. Shining boy - his name will be Cú Chulainn.

As for me, I come as I please. No one can hinder my passage. I watch in the thorn trees and between the crackle of campfire flames. When you bend to wash in a clear pool you may see me rise before you. My skin is whiter than the last patch of snow in a mountain pass. My hair is blacker than the dreamless sleep behind your eyes. My lips are berry liquor – bright blood of the dying year. Men have called me Phantom, Battle-Strife, Nightmare. I am the Great Queen, stepping in from beyond, taunting you in the reeds, in the crags, in the unstitched nothing between the stars. One fix of my emerald stare will send you mad. Drums will be in your ears and the wail of war pipes. I am Morrigan.

From his birth this Cú Chulainn is all brawl and blood. He burls into his life, shunting at his mother's thighs, gasping for the morning air. He is born when the foals are dropped into new grass. He grows quick, like a colt, outstripping all the other boys. This morning, as he steps ashore on the white coast of Alba a red vixen takes his scent as he passes, for the tang of killing already trails behind him.

He has come with Ferdiad to train under the fighting woman Scáthach. She lives in shadow, like the forest cat. Her skin is brindled with ink. She teaches these boys to strike suddenly at the neck, breaking the spine, or punching down into the tripes of men. She hisses instructions from her dark hut. At night she comes at them like a cat, so they never get full sight of her, as she rakes at their faces. The boys learn fast. In daylight they wear scabs and scratches of Scáthach's fierce lessons. They go through the moves and feints they have learned and are the nearest match for each other.

Yet Cú Chulainn always has the upper hand. He runs quicker, on the tail of the morning. His sword glitters faster in his hand. His shield thrusts with more force. And all of this is not counting his Riastrad . . .

I stand on his horizon. I am there from his first day. I see him when his name is still Setanta, walking to the house of Culann the

Smith. It is twilight. Doors are being bolted. The red sun is creeled in bare ash branches as it smoulders over the lake. Conchobar the king of Ulster will feast at Culann's table. He has watched young Setanta on the hurley field, laying the other players out with his caman. He has seen the rage come over the boy, for the older ones scorned him and with the edge of the stick and its broad blade Setanta has cracked shin bones and smashed the heads of teammates and opposition alike.

He comes now up the path between the wattle fences. His bloody caman is on his shoulder. King Conchobar, ever keen to spot a champion, has invited the golden haired boy to eat with him. Setanta is late. There is a sound of laughter and cups clashing within. But Culann has forgotten the king's invitation and thinking all the guests are present he has let free his great hound to guard the courtyard. Ox shouldered and yellow fanged the wet-jawed dog of the smith rushes out of the dusk, leaping for Setanta's face. With scarcely a thought the boy jumps a man's length backwards and throws the sliotar up. He cracks the ash and the ball shoots down the dog's red throat. The beast reels but comes at Setanta again, so he leaps a man's length forward and cleaves its skull with his caman.

Conchobar, Culann and all the retainers come out to find Setanta standing with one foot on the corpse of the hound. His haughty chin is thrust out. His golden curls are kindled in the light of their torches. Culann rues the loss of his guard dog. But straightaway broad-browed Setanta tells him that he will go and find a strong pup, and rear it as a replacement. Until that day he will gladly guard Culann's house. All this is said before the King and the men. One among them is the withy-thin druid Cathbad. He steps forward and holds his hand over the boy's head. In a voice like two branches rasping he says that Setanta will now be Culann's dog and so this will be his name - Cú Chulainn.

From this day the king keeps one eye on the boy, for he knows that war will certainly come and he will need a champion.

I am here when there are no men and women of your race at all in these islands. I see you all come. Ships on the sea. The grandfathers of Cú Chulainn, and their great grandfathers, wandering into our mists and rain. They come with a reckoning of days and hours. They thread days together, like beads on a string. In crops of barley and wheat these new people put time on the land. My tribe are tricked like children at a fair. We are banished to the distant screes; to the gnarl-choked forests and the hidden chambers of the earth.

Bite a green crab apple. Hold its sharp flesh in your teeth. Think of it bittering your mouth for always, never to be washed away. Now you will understand our long sour song. Understand that now I walk a place where the green robes of the earth are cut and sewn to your pattern.

I have gone into the shape of a crow and I perch on a branch close to where Cú Chulainn is dying. There is sweat and blood on his knotted thighs. The spear hangs from his side. It has gone deep between his ribs. He coughs more blood. His golden curls are matted and dull. Those who have survived his assault are gleeful and rattle their shields. Some of them climb up on the shoulders of their tallest comrades and are scorning him. Yet still they hang back, fearful of that great sword, dripping and shining, as he holds it above his head. His knees are braced and his belt keeps him from slumping to the churned earth. I call to him in a crow's voice, and my words jut through the jibes and jeers. 'It is at the guarding of thy death that I am, and I shall be.' He shudders and lifts his head. He knows my riddling, even though it is rasped in crow tongue. I look in his blue eye. He knows me.

And yes, I take the love of many of your young men. I come to them when they are alone in the empty places, or when the night fires are low in your round huts. I am curious, I suppose, for the feel of flesh that will one day die. My hair is like a raven's wing. My eyes are greener than the moss in a deep glade. The young men, thin in the waist and thick in the chest, pull me to them. Beneath my dark cloak my skin is like washed chalk in a cool stream. I fold around them and ride the tide of their lust. I am always on top, for, after all, I am a queen. They may slide their hands up to my breasts. They may halt me and hold my hips still in the instant of their quenching. Yet they will see nothing except the green of my eyes, when I rise before dawn. After this they will stagger and mumble and sicken, as if the silver moon has gone into in their heads.

In the sunlight of their boyhood Ferdiad and Cú Chulainn sport on the shore, and the gulls are white garlands in the blue sky above them. Scathach watches from the dark maw of her hut. They are naked these two and they are trying to throw each other. Again and again they come to fierce clutches but Cú Chulainn always pushes Ferdiad down on the white sand. To them I am nothing more than the hissing of the waves. They cannot see me although I stand close on the bare strand. I marvel at the growth in the boy. At twelve he stands like a man, tall and golden as if his limbs have been dipped in year old mead. Between his legs his cock is a dark and heavy bolt, like a lump of oak.

He may not be fully grown but already he has caused the Ulstermen to vex and pull their beards over him. They have sent Cú Chulainn to the fighting woman Scáthach in the half hope that he will be killed. For at just ten years old he demands weapons and war gear from king Conchobar. The tall warriors are all astonished when the king gives him his own sword. The druid Cathbad puts his hand over Cú Chulainn's curls and his eyes go white as he prophesies that the boy's life will be a short one. 'Better a short life with honour,' replies Cú Chulainn, smiling, as he walks away in his new armour.

Then one day word comes to him that three sons of the king of Connacht are boasting that they have killed all the great men of Ulster and that only babies and old gimmer men are left to mind the herds. Upon hearing this Cú Chulainn immediately takes

101

king Conchobar's chariot and goes out to find these braggarts.

Now I stand on a hillside and watch him coming home, haloed in the brazen dawn. There is a far off din like thunder caught in a valley. The chariot rattles. The charioteer yells the horses onward. Cú Chulainn's helmet flashes, blinding the astonished Ulstermen. There is blood on his forearms and blood striped across his face. It is the blood of the three Connacht princes who lie in pieces on the great plain. He leans back in the chariot with his arms outspread, two javelins in one hand. In the other his shield's edge is keen as a knife blade sharpened on the morning light. Drumbeats seem to rise from the earth. The ground trembles underfoot. At a gallop the horses draw the chariot in a clattering blur past the assembled warriors.

Cú Chulainn is roaring. This is the sound which is like thunder. His lips are drawn back. It is a wild cry. In his eyes elation and fury boil together, so that it is clear that he cannot tell who is a friend or who is an enemy. He jumps from the chariot and throws his weapons into the mud, and stands before the king's picked troop. He is terrible. His shirt has burst open. His eyes swivel in his head.

Cú Chulainn stamps his foot and his leg goes deep into the ground. He arches his spine and it cracks like a pine log in the frost. His battle fever is so fierce the Ulstermen fear that he will wade into them with his bare hands. They have never seen the like of this boy and they quail. But the wives and daughters know what to do. In a line they walk before him naked and call softly to him in hushing tones. Like a dog slapped when it barks at the wind Cú Chulainn's head turns to the women who sidle past him in the round glory of their flesh and the brawling blood straightaway dies in him. Yet a fresh new roar breaks from his mouth, and his thighs knot on a new torque. His hips jolt in the forward shudder of lust for the women; lust for the red haired ones, the fair ones and the dark ones. Lust for all of them.

At this moment the Ulstermen see that the golden maned boy

is distracted so the whole mob seize him and drag him to three barrels of cold water lined up by the gate. Cú Chulainn is still howling for the women when they throw him in the first barrel. The water immediately boils away at the thrash of his limbs. The Ulstermen drag him out and dunk him in the second barrel. It boils again but less so. When they place him in the third barrel, with their scalded hands, the water makes a peace against Cú Chulainn's skin and he is calmed.

From away on the hillside I see all this; how the king's best men are like children around this boy who has grown into his manhood in just twelve years. I see how his dark bod rises like a bolt of bog oak between his legs. I see the worried look on the faces of the Ulstermen, fearing for the safety of their women. I see the desire in the eyes of the naked women, wives and daughters as they parade before him. This is why the Ulstermen send him across the sea to Alba, hoping he will not return and for all this, I follow him.

Now he is dying but the jeers of his enemies are dulled because there is nothing between his eye and my eye. His eye is more blue than a clear morning above the snow on Slieabh Donairt. My eye is bright and black as beetle shell. Together we hold each other's look in the cool air between my perch and his fatal stone.

His life is all blood and conquest. Back when he is an apprentice to Scáthach the fighting woman of Alba he learns that she has a sister with whom she is always at war. Aífe is her name. Cú Chulainn asks Scáthach for permission to go and fight her. With the blessing of his mistress the boy sails to another island and seeks out Aífe in the dark trees that hem the shore. The woman is as shadowy as her sister. She comes at Cú Chulainn at night when he is making a fire. It is as if he is suddenly grappling with the muscle of the dusk, for he cannot seem to hold her fast, but when she bites his neck the pain brings up his fury and he hurls himself across the fire. He looks over his shoulder and sees her in the flicker and crackle. He turns in the air and takes hold of her

103

wrists, telling her that he will force her into the flames if she does not yield. There she is under him, spitting and as brindled as her sister. It takes her a good while to realise the strength of Cú Chulainn, yet at last she gives him the word of submission.

I am a flea and watch all this from the ear of a hare. I hear Cú Chulainn give the terms of his victory, that Aífe should give her sister peace and that she must lie with him by the fire until morning. I watch as Aífe's ankles lock around the hips of the boy.

At dawn I sit in the ear of the hare and see him sail back to Scáthach, cocky and pleased with himself. Little does he know that two killings will play out from this rutting.

My tribe is in twilight. We move slowly there and yearn for the wind and the fresh scent of crushed leaves. We are old, but I am the oldest of all my people. I find myself drawn again to this Cú Chulainn for he is a puzzle among your men; full of glory and yet caught between the tall hedges of his fate like a colt hemmed in the corral.

Scáthach whispers her pleasure from the gloom of her hut as Cú Chulainn stands at the door to tell her his news. Ferdiad is away gathering nettles. She rustles in the darkness and gives him a new weapon, telling him to furl it in his cloak and take it back to Ulster.

So on a keen morning Dark haired Ferdiad and golden Cú Chulainn push out through the surf and climb wet to the thighs into their Currach. I go with them, before and behind, at their tiller and in the water chuckling against the pitched hide of their boat.

War comes.

Medb his queen of Connacht. She hears of a great stud bull they keep in Ulster. It is told that the bull stands the height of three men at the shoulder. She hears how it shits a morass of dung daily. How it slavers cups of snot from its loose mouth and dribbles pails of warm spunk wherever it goes. The calves born in Ulster, they say, are fat and big. So Medb calls a great host of men before her in the spring, drawn from all across Ireland and she sends them off to fetch the bull back to Connacht. The queen gets itchy in her hall at the thought of this great bull among all her heifers and she looks forward to the day when it will bellow its love victory over the herd. Medb is ever a woman for the men. It takes seven of them to satisfy her at one time. She lies all day on a rug.

War on the border. War in the glens. War on the mountains. War, the red lung cry. War; strong troops coming through the passes and among the trees. But where are the Ulstermen? They are sleeping. Cursed, they snore and no one can wake them, and the women are trembling at the thought of strangers with wicked eyes, and the livestock are in rich pastures ready to be driven off into Connacht.

Yet wait. There is already fear creeping through the host that comes up to the gates of Ulster, for in ones and twos and fives and tens they are being picked off at night. The invaders quickly grow to hate the sun's setting, for wherever the path narrows between steep banks or in stands of thorn and ash trees, or at the hem of broad lakes, a foe creeps in the darkness. Sling shot takes an eye here, breaks an arm there. A man sinks to his knees at the head of a column. An iron dart has gone clean through his throat. He coughs his life out onto the green turf, as his comrades run in all directions. A big soldier from the south, brown eyed and scarred from many battles, crouches against an oak tree, his britches around his ankles. Two arms reach around the trunk and strangle him silently as he takes his last shit.

The whole army is afraid but this only makes it more angry. Eager kerns, drawn from the four corners of Ireland march quickly, thirsting for plunder. At last the host reaches a ford at midday. Quick cold water and a line of trees behind it, and the steep mountains on either side. The sky bright and the wind cold, even though it is spring time. One man stands on the other side of the ford, waiting, with his unsheathed sword resting on his shoulder. His head is down, as if in deep thought. The bull's horn trumpets of the enemy sound and the army halts. The ranks form up and dust from their march rises around their knees. Spears and shields rattle, but the men are silent. All eyes are on the figure standing across the fast water.

He moves slowly, casting off his fringed woollen cloak, then he lifts his saffron shirt over his head. Both drop to the green turf. Naked, he walks into the ford up to his knees. He looks up. This is Cú Chulainn. Let me give you to him in the noon of his prime. Like a lion etched on a golden cauldron; the sunlight is happy to glisten on his limbs as he moves. His yellow hair is shorn at the back and his fringe has grown long over his eyes. There is a wide beam to his shoulders. His hips are narrow. His skin is amber. A boy's passion glows in the frame of his manly face. He is burnished and wild to look upon. Cú Chulainn.

Now, thighs apart and head back he scans the ranks on the far bank. The water goes around his legs as if he were a rock planted mid-stream. He speaks. 'What is this sheaf of green barley stalks? What is this mewl of unweaned kittens? What is this row of crumbs.' As when on rare days when the wind is too hot and strong, his voice has a bronze clang that hurts the ears of his enemies.

Cú Chulainn harangues them again. 'I have woven my steps among yours by night. Like a reaching shadow I have killed a clutch of your chieftains, bodyguards and pot boys. It was no bother to me. I harried you with sharps of iron. Yet still you come creeping up to our gates, like girlish thieves.'

The army of Medb puts their hands over their ears. Stones begin to roll down the slopes on either side, such is the clap and rumble of Cú Chulainn's voice. But the bravest of them stand forward and shout back at him. 'We will trample you and lay waste all the halls and fields. We will take the great stud bull away and your women too, like a string of pearls roped up behind it. For who guards Ulster now?' they laugh. 'None but a boy and all the men are sleeping.'

The reply comes like a tree being felled across dry bracken. 'I guard Ulster. I hold the pass of the north, until our men waken!' Cú Chulainn spins in the ford until the sunlight through the spray is like amber on his skin. 'I will fight you one by one, if there are any among you who is man enough. So come to my arms,' he laughs, 'or slink away in disgrace.'

And so the boldest men go down the bank to the ford one by one, although every note in their heads tells them to turn back and take the cowards' path.

Javelins first. Cú Chulainn throws and his points go through one, two and three men. Then darts. Men have scarcely reached the water before they clasp their brows or their chests. They fall sideways on the shore. They come quicker, in their fury, flinging spears as they run, but Cú Chulainn leaps and twists and the shafts pass by his golden skin. He is laughing now, the boy-man, warming up, with the sweat like butter on his arms. The water is all frothing around him, for now he goes to work with his sword. Winnowing, threshing, slashing, he splits skulls, tears arms and cleaves spines. In an hour Cú Chulainn stands upon a mound of corpses, an island of white flesh in the stream. The water runs red towards the sea and the Hound of Ulster is roaring again, for they have fed his fury with blood.

No one else shows such exultation in killing except me. I am a crow watching the fray in an old gnarled apple tree. I see Cú Chulainn's skin flicker and twitch as his muscles writhe at each parry and thrust of the blade. He is quicker than the cold water and hotter than the noon-baked stones on the banks. Like a sunbeam in spring rain the champions sent against him never see the death blow.

And for weeks and months he goes about this business of swift, fluid butchery. For Medb's army cannot go back. They are caught by pride in the mill of Cú Chulainn's slaughter. At the end of each day he gathers up the heads of his enemies and wades back to his side of the ford. He hangs the heads from his chariot, from trees, on upturned spears. Then he rides through the sunset, arms outspread, his charioteer Láeg urging the horses on. Up and down the bank they race with the heads of the slain bobbing and looking sightless back across at their comrades still living on the far side. The men stare back from their ranks rueful and full of dread.

107

I see all this and grow to want the golden boy-man more than I have wanted any other...

...So one morning, when Medb's great army is resting and casting knuckle bones to decide who will go next into the ford, I come to him. Cú Chulainn rides the sprung planks of his chariot. Down from the hills; one black horse and one grey, and Láeg his charioteer stepping forward between them. Cú Chulainn is washed and has the sun on his shoulder. His spears are newly cleaned and the sharp of his sword cuts the early light. In a wide circle the horses clatter around me. The warrior and the driver, both look the length of me as they pass by.

See me now. My red dress furls tightly against my skin. My arms are moon-white. My black hair is free. I wear a cape of ravens' feathers. My eyes are green as holly leaves. I have stepped into Cú Chulainn's day through nine folds of mist. As I walk in the meadow that sweeps down to the ford I know well how my shape draws his gaze. At my back I bring fifteen cows, red eared and white flanked. They roll their eyes as they dip for the wet grass. I have made the spring flowers blossom – the blue gentian, the pink bilberry, the white bramble.

The horses buck as the chariot comes to a stop and Cú Chulainn jumps to the sward. 'Who are you?' he asks.

'The daughter of an ageless king,' I reply, low and warm and slow. 'These heifers are my tribute to you. Each one is a gem from my father's great herd.'

'Why bring them here?' asks Cú Chulainn.

'I have told you, they are my gift to you.'

'But why this gift?'

'Oh, Cú Chulainn, why do you ask? Isn't it clear to see? There is talk of you in every corner. Little boys play at being you, slashing at each other with sticks. Old men tell their families that they were as strong as you in their prime. The women of Ireland sigh like the wind in desire for you.' I draw near, my hand trailing in the meadow flowers. So close to him that I can see my face in the dark well of his pupils. My voice is like the lazy bees when they have forgotten their toils. 'And so I come to you as a princess with a promise of gifts.'

Cú Chulainn casts off his fringed cloak into the damp grass. He brushes his yellow fringe away from his face. 'These cows?' he asks, with an incline of his head.

'More,' I reply, smoothing my red dress. 'Much more.'

'What?'

'I will take you into the forest and give you love. I will take the sap of you and make you weak at midnight, but you will rise stronger than ever.'

Here is the moment of balance. We are sharing breath. My skin prickles.

But Cú Chulainn laughs and steps back. 'There is war here and I have no need of women right now.' He turns and calls for Láeg his charioteer then looks back at me. 'Go away from here. Find some fool ripe for your seduction and do not let me see your face again in Ulster.'

Scream in my head! And yellow fury as if ivy berries and yew berries are souring in my belly. Bitter, bitter rage, to be so scorned. I bite my tongue. I claw my fingers. 'You hear me, whelp of the north, no one spurns me.' Cú Chulainn is still laughing. 'I will come at you. I will stagger you in your stride. I will say these geasa over you that no one can break. You must never eat dog meat. You must never refuse food offered by a woman.' I turn sideways into the morning wind and am gone suddenly from his sight. But I see him walk away cheerful and sunny, limbering his arm for his day of fighting.

Before noon I am an eel in the fresh water where he stands slashing at his enemies. I twine against his ankles attempting to make him trip, but he steps through my coils.

Before noon I am a long grey wolf and I stampede the cattle into the stream. The water breaks all around him as the cows kick and plunge, but Cú Chulainn leaps up on their backs and so cuts the head off one of Medb's champions to boot.

Before noon I am the biggest of the red-eared heifers and I make to gore him and trample him down into the bed of the stream. But Cú Chulainn steps aside and smacks my nose with the pole of his spear. I am dazzled with splashing water and pain.

As I go he gives my words back to me, 'I come to you as a princess.' And he laughs.

Oh Cú Chulainn, blood up to your oxters, two killings will mark you more than all the others. One night the hero of Ulster is lying on his furs. All is darkness. The door to his round lodge is shut. A figure, black and low, opens it and steps inside. The solid shape of a man bends over Cú Chulainn. He is silent or nearly so, for his breath is as soft as moleskin. Yet Cú Chulainn wakes under his gaze and reaches for his furled weapon. This is the gift he has taken from Scáthach in Alba. Cú Chulainn bellows like a red deer, but much louder is the silver-dread scream that breaks from the mouth of the intruder. Cú Chulainn springs up and drags the man outside into the moonlight, where he lies choking on the grass. 'Who are you?' The man cannot speak for Cú Chulainn sees now how the pain courses through the stranger. Blood froths from his lips. He claws at his writhing belly. Cú Chulainn pours water into the man's mouth. In all his fighting he has never seen an enemy spiked with so much agony. Cú Chulainn's weapon is still deep in him. 'Who are you?' he asks again.

The stranger's voice is thick with blood, like eggs being beaten in a bowl. 'I am Connla, your son,' he answers. Now Cú Chulainn bends and sees a face of the same make of his own. The same hair, as gold as the morning. In breaking grief and astonishment Cú Chulainn takes the shuddering Connla into his arms. 'My mother is Aífe,' coughs the young man. 'I came to find you my father, but you have speared me with cruel dark poison.'

Cú Chulainn bawls tearful rage at the night sky as he clasps the son he has broken. Connla's wet muttering words die first and then he thrashes out his life against the breast of his father. Cú Chulainn rises only when the dawn comes and then he runs soaked in the blood of his son to the wild mountainside and none dare bar his way.

It is a much later day that the next killing comes to him.

Queen Medb awakens surrounded by her young lovers. It is late afternoon. The war is going badly. Even though the men of Ulster are sleeping her army is being winnowed at the ford. Medb has spent the day at her pleasures but she is unsatisfied. In the prick of her temper she thinks of a plan. She cannot wait much longer or the flower of her army will all be flayed by Cú Chulainn. So she tells her lovers to fetch a certain fighting man for a night of feasting.

He comes into the hall when the cauldron is boiling and the mead is brimming in the cups. Medb, fleshy and pale and draped in a white gown, looks him up and down. His skin is coarse and rusty and his hair is black. He is at once lithe and strong. His cloak is a swirl of purple and green. This man is Ferdiad, the foster brother of Cú Chulainn, with whom he trained in Alba. The queen of Connacht lets her gown fall. She holds a cup of the honey wine out for Ferdiad and draws him to her side. They lie together and drink. Medb's eyes are as golden and pale as September barley. At the first sip Ferdiad feels himself keeling forward and all the time her words are honeying at his ear. Up in the rafters in I watch Medb's white thigh cross the dark thigh of Ferdiad. And fair play to you girl, I say, as I watch the proceedings from my dark corner. I would do the same.

So she plies Ferdiad and she caresses him until he doesn't know himself. Then when his tongue is no longer his own she makes him give his word that he will be her champion and fight her great enemy. With mead thickened lips he gives a silly, skilly smile and promises. I must admit I admire her work.

Cú Chulainn stands washed and haloed in the morning. His yellow fringe is over his eyes. His weapons are burnished. His muscles sing in the clean light. Láeg his charioteer is standing by. Cú Chulainn is ready for the fight.

There comes a clatter on the far side of the ford and the enemy host parts to allow a chariot through. Down sweeps Ferdiad, with sore eyes and pain in all his features. To me it is strange how Cú Chulainn never foresees the looming strokes of his fate. Nevertheless, as he recognises that it is Ferdiad advancing across the plain and arrayed for battle he realises that some terrible trickery has been done.

For a moment the two of them stare at each other, then both walk unarmed into the sharp, cold water. They embrace and kiss and no one can hear the soft words they share. No-one apart from me, for I am flying as a crow in the wind above the valley and I can hear everything. Cú Chulainn asks if there is any way out of the situation. Ferdiad says that although he has been fooled, he is still bound by his word. So pressing forehead to forehead each stares into the other's eyes and they weep the tears of men who have bitter business to do.

Never has there been such a combat since mortals washed up on the shores of Ireland. Ferdiad and Cú Chulainn go to their chariots and come back with short spears and darts. They hurl at each other all day and each of them are equal in skill and strength, so that the spears glance off their shields and the darts chime point on point. The water breaks against their thighs and each man, the dark and the golden, is a flashing blur in the eyes of the host drawn up on the bank. All this first day they are completely unwounded and when the sun reddens they throw their weapons back at their charioteers and wade to the centre of the ford. Here they embrace again, arms wrapped around necks, cheeks together. Then the charioteers make beds of rushes, mint and daisies so that Cú Chulainn and Ferdiad can rest. They go to and fro across the stream taking food to the weary champions. As night falls the charioteers sit around the same fire and the four horses are tied together.

Sunrise comes like a laughing coin and the two men rise refreshed. In the stream they embrace like brothers who have been sundered for year. Today they use spears with long points and hefty shafts. This is closer business and now the blooding be-

112

gins. Jump and twist and jab, they fight until the wind changes and evening hoves across the mountains. Both Cú Chulainn and Ferdiad have wounds that would kill any normal man. The clean white of their bones are laid bare amid the chopped meat of their gashes. The water of the ford is streaked with crimson. Throwing aside their weapons they draw close and hold themselves against the other's torn flesh for a long while. Then they stagger to their own sides of the ford.

As before the charioteers do their best to make the champions comfortable. They share herbs and ointments to dress the wounds. Again the charioteers sit at the same fire while Cú Chulainn and Ferdiad sleep. The horses are tethered in the same corral.

Cock crow shudders everyone awake to the chill of the new morning. Cú Chulainn rises fresh and bright. His wounds are nearly healed. He steps down to the water. His moustache is long. His fringe sits low over his blue eyes and the sun is behind him. But as Ferdiad comes Cú Chulainn sees straightaway that he is moving like a man stitched together from the parts of several corpses. Jerkily and shuffling he wades through the water. Cú Chulainn goes to him and in his low deep, voice he talks to Ferdiad in words no one else can hear. No one except me, as I course the rise of the wind above them. For the last time Cú Chulainn begs Ferdiad to call off the fight. He casts up memories of their shared youth, when they were like pups sharing the same bed, tugging at the same blankets, sleeping safe in the same warmth. Ferdiad's eyes are close to Cú Chulainn's and they are gloomy. In a hushed voice he replies that he cannot break the oath he has made to Medb.

They take up their weapons.

Beaten swords are serpent licks in the early light. They go clash for clash. Sweat and blood mist the air around their flashing arms. Now also there are cries of pain, but these are all from Ferdiad. When at last the light falters they throw down the blades and each stumbles to his own side of the ford. This time they do not embrace and the charioteers make up their

113

own fires. The horses chomp in separate pastures. All night the sleepless Ferdiad presses his wounds and tries to staunch them.

He rises in the grey time before dawn when the sky is milky. He straps on plates of boiled leather and bronze knowing that armour is his only hope to win the combat. Cú Chulainn comes down to the ford and finds Ferdiad standing in the early mist pale and haggard like a man cast up from the land of the dead.

Shields and short swords. The splinter and crack of wood, and the grunts of the pair in the stream waken Medb's soldiers who come to watch. Cú Chulainn fights naked. His face is like a stone as he hacks at Ferdiad. I am a crow above them. I scream crow curses across the valley. For an instant I put my shadow between Cú Chulainn and the sun. He looks up and Ferdiad takes his chance. He plunges a dagger into Cú Chulainn's side up to the hilt. Cú Chulainn buckles and falls into the ford. Dark Ferdiad's face flickers with the surge of victory. But the water heaves and Cú Chulainn leaps to his side of the bank. He bellows like a bull for Láeg his charioteer to hand him the furled spear given to him by Scáthach. With black blood streaming from the space between two ribs Cú Chulainn's battle fever comes upon him. He clenches his fists and the bones of his fingers crack. He arches his spine and the sound is like ice splintering in spring. His eyes are boiling slits and his mouth is stretched wide to bare his sharpest teeth.

Láeg tosses Cú Chulainn the spear and then makes a run for it. He knows that Cú Chulainn is now past recognising friend from enemy. The valley shakes with Cú Chulainn's raging. All this happens quicker than mortal men can see. So Ferdiad is still standing mid-stream thinking he has won, when a sudden piercing agony threshes every fibre of his body. He claws at his chest and coughs up gobbets of flesh.

Cú Chulainn watches as Ferdiad kicks at the water and dashes his against the stones on the bank. It is Cú Chulainn's moment of victory but no one can watch such pain and remain unmoved. The battle-rage quickly passes. He has thrust a nightmare shaft into the guts of his oldest friend. Its name is Gáe Bulg - the 'dread spear.' Notched and cruel, splayed with barbs and venomous too, the head of the weapon has eaten into Ferdiad. His armour is no proof against the spear and now the sharps are rasping in all his joints. Lightning walks in him. The Gáe Bulg can never be withdrawn from a living body, for it will pull the tripes of the wounded man inside out.

Blood erupts from every opening in Ferdiad's impaled body. His face goes white with torment. Cú Chulainn bends to his friend and carries him to his own side of the ford so that he will die in Ulster. Ferdiad's fingers bite deeply into the arms of Cú Chulainn. I flutter down and sit preening nearby. I hear the words shared. Cú Chulainn bends over his friend who is twitching in sudden fever and a thicket of pain. 'Hush my brother,' he whispers, 'this was foully ordered.'

'I kept my word' says Ferdiad and his hands are in Cú Chulainn's hair.

'That you did' Cú Chulainn replies, 'And look at where it has got you. But peace now, peace to you.'

'I am going my way,' Ferdiad stutters, and then his eyes become dull.

Cú Chulainn rocks the corpse back and forth until Láeg comes to him. 'We must away,' says the charioteer. 'Medb's army will soon lose their fear and you are in no mood for more fighting. Cú Chulainn nods and then carries the body of Ferdiad in silence towards his chariot. Láeg looks around and then shoos me off. 'Get lost black crow' he shouts. 'Pluck your old feathers elsewhere. You shall have no carrion tonight.' It is almost as if he knows me. Almost.

I carp back at him in words he cannot understand. 'Careful boy. I will see you in another of your days.' As I flap up the stairs of the grey wind I am full of rasping laughter, for it is almost as if I have woven this bloody tryst between the two friends myself.

Ferdiad's last words - Going my way. Where do you people go when breath leaves you? What is this journey you make? I shrug

115

this off and fly into the east.

Cú Chulainn puts his back to Medb's army and he vows never to use the Gáe Bulg again. The invaders think the way is open and they flash their spears eagerly. But the men of Ulster have woken from their slumbers and come down through the glens in great numbers. Cú Chulainn retires and takes no more part in the war of the Great Bull.

The days of winter are here when I step into a morning. My red dress flames on my white skin. My black hair is night water in a sea cave. My feet are bare and it is good to walk on the frost-brittle grass. A mountainy place; I recognise the jag of the old peaks above me but I know they have new names now.

Here is a young shepherd. His hair is as tawny as that of a fawn. He wears a long fleece coat. When he sees me his chops fall open. There are frozen lips of ice on the edge of the stream. The sheep are down drinking feet-first on the banks. All is calm and the shepherd stands as if he is frozen to his lookout stone. I go to pass him by, but think twice. I reach for his hand. Long fingers with dirt under the nails curl in mine. I lead him to a patch of sunlight. I slide his fleece off his shoulders and we lay down upon it. He never says a word, even when I hitch my dress up and sit across his hips, even when I rock and moan above him, he says nothing. He only cries out once and then is silent. I lie beside him for while, until he stands bare-arsed and staggers stilty legged back to his flock. He has a distant and pallid look on his face. He will be deathly sick before nightfall. Good.

There is peace again between the tribes of men. The cattle are penned and Cú Chulainn is resting behind the palisades of his fortress. However, Medb of Connacht is restless. She works on a long grudge against the champion of the north until she cannot sleep and her whole pack of lovers are nearly broken in trying to satisfy her. Medb knows that there are fathers, brothers and sons who are hungering for vengeance too. They wear disgrace and pain of loss like slave chains. So she calls them all together and lies waiting on her rugs.

Fire before dawn. Children running from dripping blades. Dogs crawling speared in the boreens. Cú Chulainn wakes from a red and black dream where all is havoc. He can smell smoke on the wind. Naked, he runs to his gate and sees the orange glow of burning far away to the south. His eyes are glassy and full of the flames when he turns to Láeg who has come to his side. 'What is this?' asks Cú Chulainn.

'I cannot tell if it is a phantom clamour or a real army,' the charioteer replies.

Now Cathbad the Druid comes up. He is like an old heron. Sniffing the dawn he says, 'My hunch is that this will be no good for you Cú Chulainn. Remember the old geasa over you.'

Cú Chulainn smiles and pushes his gold fringe from his blue eyes. 'None of that now' he says. 'Láeg, make the horses ready.'

As the sun rises the charioteer attempts to yoke the horses but they are both rearing and frothing. One is Liath Macha, a grey stallion. It refuses to be backed up in the harness. Láeg calls for Cú Chulainn and the two of them wrestle the horse until it is secure against the shaft. The other is Dub Sainglend, a black stallion. It kicks out and tosses its head, resentful of the bit. Nevertheless, soon they are both buckled and tightened. When Cú Chulainn steps up Láeg looks back at him points to Liath Macha. There, dark against the grey, tears of blood trickle from its eyes. 'This is a bad sign,' he says ruefully.

'Ach, all this worry is for old wives,' says Cú Chulainn, clutching his spears. 'Come, let us drive into the south. There are voices of pain and rage down there.'

And so they go, with the sun on Cú Chulainn's broad back, and Láeg crouching in front. Pebbles spatter from the wheel-rims. The horses are glossy. Women crowd at the gates until the chariot

117

is lost from sight.

I stand on a hill between two yew trees. My eyes are as green as new grass. I am whiter than milk and my hair is black as thunder. Of all men Cú Chulainn is the only one ever to refuse me. How long can the thorn of my rage prick? I'll show you.

I saunter after him on the trail that leads towards the Great Plain.

Shadows and rocks. Corpses opened for the wolf and the fox to tug. I thrill in the stench of carrion. Women and children lie by the roadside. Stockades are scorched and broken. Cú Chulainn and Láeg ride into a land of death. He has no idea that all this has been done to lure him out. I say again, he never sees it coming. This is all Medb's scheme, but I also have a part to play.

Láeg is watering the horses in a fast-running stream. He looks up to see an old woman washing bronze armour and dented weapons in the bone-chill torrent. She has one tooth in her grey gums and one grey eye. Her hair straggles over her face. Her skin is like soiled linen. She croons a silly old song. Láeg pulls the horses back suddenly when he sees blood running in the water, down from where the woman is crouched. 'Who is that?' asks Cú Chulainn.

'I don't know' replies Láeg, 'But I think it is your bloody armour she is washing. We should turn back, for it is a warning.'

'We won't turn back just because some old biddy is doing the laundry,' says Cú Chulainn, clapping his charioteer on the back.

Láeg looks up again and sees that the woman has gone. Only the sound of thin laughter on the wind proves she has been there at all. 'This is no good,' he mutters under his breath. You have to give Láeg his dues here; I think he recognises a look in the crone's eye. It is the same look in the eye of the crow he shoos away from the corpse of Frediad. For, of course, I am the hook-chinned old washerwoman with blood up to my elbows.

Now I am out of this garb I watch from the peaks as the chariot rattles away and Cú Chulainn's gold face is set on a new battle-tryst, about which he knows nothing. Láeg, however, scans the horizon uneasy, watchful as a woken owl. Turn and turn go your days Cú Chulainn. You are riding to your death. No one can hear me. All is in place, all is good, but something must be broken in order for the circle to be completed.

It is nothing for me to turn sideways into the wind and give myself a new shape. Round face and gentle smile; another old woman, this one like a grandmother that children visit for soup and honey cakes. Laughing eyes and red pudgy hands, I am sitting by a simmering pot when the chariot approaches. The road is narrow. I wait with my feet stretched over the dry ruts of the track, and so the chariot slows. As I look up, the sheen on Cú Chulainn's breastplate nearly blinds me. His hair is clean and golden. His lips are red as haws. His arms are knotted thick, like oak boughs. The clear day is in his face as he asks Láeg to halt. He jumps to the road and comes to me laughing. 'Now, now granny' he says. 'You need to keep your old feet out of the way.' Here he is, tapered down to his strong haunches. Thighs like living marble and the bod mor of him in between, like a heavy hammer.

'Still eager as a colt, I see Cú Chulainn,' I wheedle in my old crumpled voice. In my head I say here is a man to keep a woman warm in midwinter. A man you could ride all night and never break him. A strong colt. 'Come and have some food' my mouth says.

'I have eaten,' he says. 'But it has been said over my head that I am never to refuse food offered by a woman. So just a bite please, for the sake of courtesy.'

'Aye aye, a big man needs his stew,' I gimmer back at him. 'Here.' I reach out a wooden ladle and Cú Chulainn bends to eat, with me smiling and chewing my old gums.

He takes a swallow and a grey look passes over his face. 'That's coarse and bitter meat.'

'Aye aye,' I am still smiling at him. 'It's the pluck of a beast, with green flesh and sour fat. A dead beast already picked over by the kites.'

'And you cook this rotten flesh up to give to strangers granny?' asks Cú Chulainn. He is retching now and hawking. I see Láeg is concerned.

'Dog flesh!' I spit back. And now I rise out of my guise. The face of the cherry cheeked old woman falls away and I am myself again. Dark and white and red, I reach out my long fingers. Cú Chulainn reels away like a salted snail. The horses jump in their traces. 'Dog flesh for the Hound of Ulster.' My laughter is a falcon's cry. 'Cú Chulainn eats himself!' Láeg throws a stone but it goes through me as if I am made of smoke. I am already in the sky and in the thorn trees and hidden from their eyes.

Cú Chulainn hangs his head, then he kicks at the stewpot. He knows that the geasa has been broken. It is death for him. Death there, down the corpse littered track to the south. His ear pricks at the wail of war pipes and he goes once more to his chariot. They drive towards the Great Plain.

Go again Cú Chulainn, Go again through the ranks of your enemies. Yes, go again. There are men who prick their skin with ink to make the shapes of animals on their legs and arms. Cú Chulainn stripes his skin red with sticky carnage. You know that I lust after this boy, for his haughty chin, his wide shoulders and his blue stare. But what gets me wet in the oily night between my legs is the way he hews men. I say again, no one draws more lust from the havoc of battle and carrion than me.

A blow to his mouth has broken his teeth but still he laughs and roars. Leaning and lunging in the chariot he sweeps his iron sword, and heads are flung into the wind. Fear and anger are in the eyes of his the host arrayed against him. Fury is on the tongue of Lugaid who has come for vengeance. Cú Chulainn has no notion as to why this army has drawn up on the Great Plain. No idea that it has murdered and pillaged and burnt its way to the place of the Standing Stone simply to draw him out. Queen Medb has sown her plans well.

Lugaid is a rangy Munster man whose sons suffer Cú Chulainn's sword in the War of the Great Bull. Split navel to jaw, their blood drains into the ford. So Lugaid needs little goading. Medb doesn't even take him to bed. She just finds him the most skilful, cunning blacksmith in the land. Then she calls all those men whose sons and fathers have been spiked and slashed by the Hound of Ulster. And a big army it is. The screaming of the pipes infects men's bodies with the dance of war. They cannot resist the jump and urging of the reels. When the piper plays men take leave of their reason.

But the old frenzy has come over Cú Chulainn. It is not music that rouses him. It is the stink of spilled guts and the death shrieks of men and the tearing of his own wounds which drives him completely mad. This is the Riastrad – Cú Chulainn's storming, mindless ecstasy. Láeg hunkers low in the chariot, mindful that his master is beyond all sense and he is fearful that Cú Chulainn will slice his head off with little regard.

The bindings of Cú Chulainn's breastplate have snapped. He chews his tongue with his broken teeth. His voice is like a cracked bull's horn trumpet. His spears go through three men at once and for each of them Cú Chulainn bellows joyfully. Snot and blood flies from his nose and Láeg looks up, knowing there is more rage to come. So far it has all been up and down the ranks, with the chariot pelting in front and Cú Chulainn batting away the darts and spears thrown against him. He looks at the litter of hands and feet on the mashed grass. He is panting and his eyes have an icy bleb. Red bones and scalped men and hamstrung men lie before him and the enemy host. With a growl he signals for Láeg to charge. Now come the three thunder feats for which Cú Chulainn's name is known even your days.

See him in his glory for one last time. His sword smokes white hot and the blinding sun is on his shoulder. His golden fringe is like a mantle of the dawn. Three times he crashes through Medb's army, leaving a wreckage of flesh. Three times he parts the kerns and sends them running pell mell. Cú Chulainn is a mess of pricked wounds. He pulls darts from his arms and throws them back. The rumbling from his hoarse throat makes the earth tremble. A dark broken is cloud frets above the Great Plain and it is through this that I come night feathered and drinking the tang of battle. I am as eager as an urgent lover and know I will not be disappointed by this final rapture.

Medb's army breaks before Cú Chulainn's onslaught. Even brave men cannot face his savagery. As they begin to run Cú Chulainn races behind, cutting them down. It is now that Lugaid steps forward. He has three spears. Each one is the exact make of Cú Chulainn's Gáe Bulg. Each one a glinting thicket of barbs. Secret spears forged in a hidden smithy. Lugaid braces himself in the sprung turf and shouts to anyone listening 'Three spears for three kings!' Cú Chulainn storms down on him. Lugaid squints his eye and hurls the first. It catches Láeg in the breast. He is flung to the earth. Cú Chulainn seizes the reins and halts the chariot. He takes Láeg in his arms. He tries to pull the barbs but they have gone deep. Láeg coughs his darkest heart's blood and dies. 'One for the king of charioteers,' grins Lugaid.

Cú Chulainn runs back to the chariot for his weapons. But Lugaid hurls again. This spear goes over Cú Chulainn's shoulder and strikes the grey stallion that rears and screams. The horse is kicking the chariot to pieces. Cú Chulainn unyokes it as best he can and sends it running away to the west, the poison spike hanging from its side. 'The second for Liath Macha, the king of horses,' laughs Lugaid.

Now he hefts and twirls his last spear and as Cú Chulainn runs toward him with a dread cursing cry, he hurls it.

The Hound of Ulster makes no show of pain as the blow sends him head over heels. He staggers up and tries to draw the spear from his belly. Eye to eye Lugaid watches as Cú Chulainn pulls, and sees that his guts are coming out with the barbs. He soon ceases this for a fool's game. The cry goes across the field that Cú Chulainn is stricken. Those who have fled begin to return. Yet greater is Lugaid's cry, 'A third spear for the King of Champions.'

Cú Chulainn's voice is as dry as tinder moss. He gasps, 'Let me drink.'

'Go on ahead,' replies Lugaid drawing his sword. 'All will be settled soon enough.'

Cú Chulainn stumbles to a muddy pool and scoops water to his broken lips. He looks around, as a cool shadow is laid across his back. It is the standing stone. I am circling above and suddenly I grow dizzy with the spectacle. Here is the consummation coming, coming, coming. He rises and lurches towards the rough sarsen. It gleams white in the late afternoon. Oh Cú Chulainn, you cannot see the hidden runes graven on its blunt faces. Ancient beyond mortal memory, the runes tell the story of your life and your death.

Medb's soldiers are drawing around hissing and yelping. Here is a change of fortune for them. They smell triumph; a great killing, to go home and tell their wives. I am nearly swooning on the wind as Cú Chulainn draws himself up and unbuckles his belt. In one move he throws it around the stone and ties himself to it. His back is towards Ulster. He will die on his feet, facing his enemies.

They are ranged in front. The smaller men climb upon the shoulders of the biggest and spit at Cú Chulainn across the grass. They press forward but there is a good gap between them and the stone. Still they are afraid of him. Even Lugaid standing out in front is hesitant. He is trembling.

Cú Chulainn raises his arm and holds his sword high. The blade shivers with light. Behind the pillar the black stallion is kicking against smashed chariot. I flutter down in my glossy feathers and sit upon a thorny branch. My crow voice is like two pebbles clacking. He raises his head. Behind his sweat-waxed fringe his eyes are glazing but he knows me.

Cú Chulainn …friend-killer…son-killer…it is at the guarding of your death I am…what could I have given you…the dues of a king…treasure…night passion…a cloak of golden silk… you know that even without my geasa you would have been here

123

lashed to this stone…blood frothing from your belly…always it would have happened…always…I am always…I can see it all… have seen it…now I drink the ravage of your life…as I have eaten the wet meat of all the men you have broken…you were made for this day above all others…you were a bolt from the golden sun…I come to attend you boy…It is coming on late…

…so now go.

In my sequin crow eye I see Cú Chulainn smiling at me. Then his head lolls and all is done with him. I hop across to perch on his shoulder. I look at him sideways. He is still. Yet even now his sword is raised above his head. I shuffle closer, the closest I have ever been to him. His enemies are silent. They watch me as I pick one of his blue eyes from its socket, and then I spread my wings to fly above and beyond the reach of men, but I look back and see how Lugaid takes his cue from my last intimacy. Only now does he find the courage to approach the sagging body. At this, his comrades renew their war chants and rattle their shields. Big men now he is dead. Quickly Lugaid gathers Cú Chulainn's hair in his fist and then hacks off the head. Yet just as quickly Cú Chulainn's upheld sword falls and cuts Lugaid's hand off at the wrist.

In the storm wrack I pass through broken clouds to the rocks and the water where no man has ever trod. Green eyes and black hair, white skin. I am a queen.

O'Carolan

One August evening, just over three hundred years ago, a boy with curly hair was passing the rath and he decided to climb up and look at the evening coming on over the fields. As he sat against the hawthorn a slow, weary doze came over him. He lay back and with the sun fading he fell into a deep sleep. All night the shapes and colours of a wild music threaded his dreams. Also he heard lamenting and singing. Now it was as desperate as a winter gale. Now it was as happy as a wedding morning.

He awoke in the cold hour, shivering under a sheet of dew. He was sore and exhausted, as though he had woken from a long illness, but his head was still full with the colours of the dream music and his fingers itched with a thrilling clamour. He ran to the nearest town and spent all his money on a new harp.

He sat in a public house and ran his hands over the strings and, although he had never played before, he found sweet and strange music uttering forth. The boy's name was Turlough O'Carolan. He went on to be the last and greatest of all the musical bards of Ireland. He played for peasants and kings He was welcome in hovels and castles. The music that uttered from his harp strings was like laughter in the glens; tears around a turf fire. It could summon a man to fight. It would break a woman's heart.

This was the precious fairy gift to O'Carolan; music that seemed to pour from the stones in a mountain stream, or the cries of fledgling larks on the first morning of flight. But a gift from the

'Good People' is a tricksy thing. A year and a day after his night rapture on the little hill O'Carolan was suddenly and emphatically struck with blindness. For the rest of his life his fingers plucked and fanned his dreams into quicksilver rills of tunes, but in all his travels, the length and breadth of Ireland he was led by a servant. The fairies had given his fingers the power of great music, but they stole away his sight.

Then again, perhaps the blindness was merely part of their gift. For while no one can say why the fairies reward or punish, and to whom they will give or take, what is certain is that their generosity comes with unforeseen consequences; caveats of mischief and discomfort, like thorns pricking under the petals of a fresh cut rose.

Peggy Colligan and the Bucket

*M*y grandfather told me that he once knew an old woman who lived away in the bogs. Her name was Peggy Colligan. Her husband had gone to his rest and her only daughter was away in service in England. One day Peggy came home from town with a bright and shiny bucket. Galvanised it was from top to toe, as if it was made of pale beaten silver. Of course Peggy knew that the lovely sheen on her bucket would soon go dull, but she felt very happy in the moment of first having it. She kept a goat for milking and she had great anticipation of the thought of the bucket full to the brim.

I think the clean newness of the bucket was the chief reason for the attention it attracted. It all happened this way; Peggy was dozing by her fire and the bucket was by the door. About midnight there came three loud little knocks, followed by a voice, like a child's or that of a young woman faraway.

'Mrs Colligan, Mrs Colligan!' piped the voice. 'Could we have the lend of your fine new bucket?'

Peggy jumped up. 'Yes surely,' she replied 'But I'll need it for the morning.' She lifted the bucket and opened the door, and wasn't the least surprised to find no one there at all. Nevertheless, Peggy put the bucket down in the darkness and went to bed.

She rose early next morning and found her bucket washed and clean outside in the wet grass by her door. Peggy shrugged and went to milk her goat. And much milk she got from the beast. Later that night, she was sitting in her chair and the turf was wan-

131

ing in her grate. Suddenly she was roused by three knocks and a little faraway voice.

'Mrs Colligan, Mrs Colligan, can we have your new bucket again?'

Peggy walked to the door saying, 'Surely, surely, but I'll want the use of it the morning.'

There was nothing outside but a soft wind coming across the bog. Peggy put the bucket down, drew her bolt and went to bed.

She rose early and there was the bucket, washed, polished and glinting like a silver shilling on her doorstep. Peggy went to the goat and got a fine draught of milk from it. That day she made some cheese and by nightfall she was weary. On the tip of midnight, when Peggy was snoring and the turf was little more than embers there came again three knocks and a little voice at her door.

'Mrs Colligan, Mrs Colligan,' cried the faraway voice. 'Can we take your new bucket until the morning?

'Surely,' replied Peggy, 'but I'll need it by the clear light of dawn.'

She opened her door and saw nothing in starless night. She placed the bucket down and went to her warm blanket. In the morning Peggy stretched and went outside in the fresh hour just after sunrise. However, although she looked everywhere, this time there was no sign of her lovely galvanised bucket. Peggy had to milk her goat into an old cracked jug and nothing but a splash she got from the animal.

Now Peggy was generally slow to anger and polite at all times, but the theft of her bucket smouldered throughout the day. By midnight she was pacing up and down her cabin and getting herself up into a most powerful righteous fury. At last she took her shawl and went away to a little green hill beyond a hedge and over a wall. Peggy stood in front of the hill with darkness all around her. She took a great breath in order to give air to her anger, but just as she was about to speak a little voice sprang up from inside the hill.

'Here, who's that coming up now?'

'No one,' another little voice in the hill replied. 'No-one, save that old woman from the Land of the Dead who wants her bucket back!'

'Well she shan't have it,' Chipped in the first voice.

'I will have it,' shouted Peggy. 'It's mine.'

'Go away,' shrieked the two tiny voices and a sudden strong wind blew into Peggy's eyes, so she made her way home.

In the morning Peggy Colligan took her old cracked jug and went out to milk her goat. On her doorstep she found her bucket, but it had been bashed and dashed and wrenched. It was dull and dirty and looked like it was a hundred years old.

The Lennan Sidh

*I*n the west of Ireland you can never tell what the weather will be from one hour to the next. Sometimes the elements will shift even more quickly, so you will walk through curtains of rain and in between you will stand in the finest new-washed sunlight. You look around and the mountains behind are suddenly smothered in slow buffering mists. The teeth of the crags in front of you are sawing cleanly against a forget-me-not sky. To the sides of the road there are glens where the shale is as dark as dragon armour, and the water slinks like a sump of quicksilver. However, pass through another veil of rain and all is re-conjured. What was grey is now blue. The slopes that were glad in the breath of the morning are now bled and dour.

In the seventeenth century Cromwell, with his hatred and implacable convictions, tramped through the land with a Bible in one hand and a sword in the other. He told the Irish to get 'to Hell or Connacht'. They were driven into this land of tricksy storms, of scoured mountains and scrubby pastures. When at last they came to the cliffs that rise above the western ocean they knew they could run no further, so they turned to eke their lives in places where even goats had trouble finding sustenance.

A man with ragged hair is walking a road of sharp stones. The wind limmers the icy waters of a loch into chipped slate peaks. His brogues are torn and his raw heels rise from the sodden leather. He has wrapped a ragged cloak of saffron wool around his shoulders, but it is heavy from the rain and he trembles. He seems to be grinning, but his lips are drawn back from his gums with fever and the chill. It is as if he has taken his pallor from the dull light on the surface of the puddles. He looks for some place to rest but everything is broken and bare here. Not one tree to sit under. This place is like a foundry of rock. He is dying and he knows it.

We will not give him a name, since he is lost to history. He will lie in this deserted pass and no one will find his body. It is the year 1660 and there are perhaps a hundred of his type wandering the roads of Ireland. He is a bitter and mournful man. You look into his eyes and the death pangs of a whole way of life, the ruin of a whole culture, stab back at you. The world has turned on him. His certainties have all been torn and scattered. He has seen the dispensations of an ancient profession forfeited by conquest.

For this man is a bard: a court poet of the Gaelic aristocracy, keeper of the genealogies, satirist and craftsman of words. His time has only just passed. He remembers, as if it were yesterday, the firelight in castle halls; nights when they listened as he told the glories of his chieftain – verses embroidered with assonance, half rhyme and slanting rhyme, allusion; metres as strict as advanced trigonometry. These were the tools of his art. He was schooled as a boy in poetic forms reaching back, in unbroken succession, all the way to the verses of the druids. He can summon hundreds of poems to his tongue. They are all stored like golden vestments in the chest of his skull. He can speak Latin, French, a little Spanish and about a dozen words of English.

But now all is all cast down. The castle, where he was an honoured retainer, was smashed by Puritan canons. His chieftain is in exile. Now his poems are as useless as silk shoes on a sow. He knows of no other life, save that of his calling, and the calling of a Gaelic bard is one that the world no longer needs.

He stands on his stilty legs and wheels about in the desolation of the wild valley. He takes himself off the road and starts to climb up the slope among the boulders and bracken. In an hour he has scrabbled high up on the mountainside. He is muttering and shivering like an old crow. When he coughs it is as though some mechanism has broken in his lungs. He speaks some words to the stones, then sinks slowly to his knees. The sun is fading and the shadows are coming like dark spears along his narrow path. He lies down, still murmuring, all alone.

But he is not alone.

From the ridge above him steps a woman. She comes always at the very moment he drifts into sleep. This evening it is a sleep that even his terrible coughing will not hinder. Everything about this girl is absolute, so please forgive my recourse to old, time-worn expressions. She is barefoot. Her toes are tiny. Her skin is keenly white, like a jug of new milk left out in the rain. Her hair is dark, darker than a starless sky. Her cheek bones are sharp. Her eyes are sapphires where swims a shoal of minnow-flecks. She bends over the bard, crooning a low whispering song. Her voice is like laurel leaves hushing. Her breath is like rubbed laurel leaves. Her dress is the gleam of laurel leaves. It is the twilight – the coineascar – but her black hair makes a sudden night over his face.

It has been this way for three years or more. In ditches, in the rubble of wrecked churches, in the huts of peasants, wherever he lies down, she is there. The first night of his wandering found him on a hillside in Mayo. He had nowhere to go. In haughty dudgeon he bought oatcakes from a woman and ate them in the growing cold. He had no wood for a fire. A bard forced to tramp the roads! Such was his fury at having to sleep in the open, if his words had been sparks that evening the heather around him would have kindled and he would have flared like a beacon, whelmed by the sulphur of his own curses. He hunkered in his fringed mantle and, after hours of tossing, fretted into chilled doze.

That first time she came up from the far side of the hill. In his dream he knew this. He saw her rise from the bushes and step lightly to his side. Behind his eyelids it was a fine spring morning. She knew his name. She spoke it back to him as she told her sorrows. There was no one to care for her, she said. She was lost in shadows. She grieved in echoing glens.

'Ochon,' she sighed, 'Ochon.'

He reached to brush her cheek. What age was she, eighteen, twenty? Deserted in bitter country. His finger touched one of her tears and suddenly it was a cold winter's day behind his eyelids. Rooks in the bare trees. She knew his misery. She spoke it back to him. 'The English have come,' she said. 'I know they are felling the forests. The Sasanaigh have scattered the Princes. The soldiers of the Gael are in their graves or lost from the land. Ochon.'

At her right shoulder was a silver penannular etched with twisting spirals. She stood up and unclasped the pin. Her gown fell at her feet. He opened his cloak and she sidled along the length of him. Their flesh made a hot seam between them. 'Give me poems, Bard,' she whispered. 'Make me live in this world.'

He shuddered awake to an autumn morning that promised nothing. All night he had known the secrets of the woman; the cleft behind her ear, the bow strung nape of her neck. But now he coughed among thistles. Dry mouthed and queasy, as if he had been drunk, he stumbled down the road. She was gone as if she had never been there at all, and there was not so much as a spailpín's hut in sight.

He walked that day as if he had not slept. His feet dragging, his arms like stiff lumber. But his eyes blazed, for he had a new flaring stanza on his tongue. It had come to him fully formed with the dawn. I will render them in English as closely as I can.

The red moon hid below the hill
In the land of clan O'Malley.
They who are gone now on the waves to Spain.
It is comfort they gave me often.

I met a girl, in the wild land, straight, tall and blue-eyed,
Her forehead pale as a white banner.

140

Pearl shouldered –
She lay skin to skin with me.

So it was, every evening after that, as soon as he lay down she was there, whispering, softly cajoling, giving him her love and moaning as he whispered back to her his verses. He could not deny her, her fingers flickering down his back. He had no power to forbid her.

Her kisses as sharp as melt water
From the highest stream.
Kisses like a new ring of silver.
Kisses like a swan breaking the morning water
Of the loch ...

He set himself up as a teacher. For, under Cromwell's laws, no children were to be permitted an education. With immense chagrin he took little coins, bread and buttermilk in payment from half-starved families. He attempted to teach rhetoric, Euclid and the high Gaelic poems to boys who smirked and cheeked him. He schooled them in the open air in the lee of a rock but the rain ran down his face and into his mouth. He built a hovel of sods and wattles and rocked in front of a tiny fire shedding furious, desperate tears.

Yet as soon as he curled on the earth floor she entered. He had grown as thin as a bundle of loose reeds. His hair was lank. His lips were cracked. But she called him her prince and she was beautiful. She knew he had eaten at the chieftain's table, knew he had tasted the strong wines of France, knew he had once worn brocades of silk and slept before a well-lit hearth.

She let her black hair free
Into a wind of cold echoes.
Secrets, secrets she told me.
Oh, mouth of honey and thyme.

141

Promises rare as apples on a spring tree,
Rare as a song on the lip
Of a salmon . . .

At first he did not notice. In the face of all his miseries he trembled with expectancy each time he settled for sleep. True, he rose each morning with a glowering despair and a hollow weakness in his limbs. But he craved her coming, hungered for the glide of her breasts against him. Those nights her words came to him distantly as though she was speaking through a woven tunnel of rowans. She was a queen. She cried in wild lands. She could only taste and touch the world through his verses. She begged him for more.

He quit his hovel and left the sullen boys to their games. He wandered further into the west, into the land of wet pewter and silver light. He shook inwardly with anger when he was forced to beg scraps of food. He offered to pay with old poems and courtly songs but the people had no use for his words. Some scorned him; others took pity and gave the soaking man a place to sleep. But when they awoke to find him thrashing and groaning and caressing the empty air they threw him into the night.

Soon he began to shun even the cabins of the poor. He rested wherever he could find enough dry branches and a nook between the stones. Still she came, crooning in her far-off words of opals and moonstones as she twined her body with his. By now he knew he was sick. His days were spent shuffling along rough tracks.

Her hair was the pennant of winter
And I thought I looked back
From a drifting galley
At the harbour lights
Of Galway of the tribes
And we were two ropes coiled in the dark hold.

Yet, in truth we never left
The green slopes near Cruach Phádraig
And the stars were stilled
And her kisses tingled like nettles after the sting
And I awoke deserted.

I was rankled, even more ruined
And left to proceed like a sentence half uttered.
A jacket half buttoned.
Wine half drunk …

He began to feel empty in his head, slack in his legs. A man can get lost in gazing for trout in a stream. Eventually he is not troubled by the prickling of thorns, nor the heat of the day. The man gazes through clear water and the fish rises and bows her beautiful back against invisible currents. The man is beyond pondering. His mind is all glancing light as he sees the trout flexing in her clear tresses, like the smile of a girl who comes freshly laughing from mass with her friends.

For three years the bard has been the wellspring from which she has quenched her thirst. Three years of tramping in cruel weather have broken him. He would run from her if he could but he knows his legs could no longer carry him far enough. He has grubbed for birds' eggs and snails. He has eaten them raw, but now he does not eat at all. He does not notice the mould blotting his saffron cloak, or his teeth rocking in his gums.

Now back to the darkness in the steep glen.

The bard's eyes flutter back into their sockets. His breathing is faint and fast, like that of a stricken hare. His last dream is shuttered by waking moments.

He would run if he could – away from her – to Scotland, the isles, where there are chieftains still who give dues and dignity to poets. Perhaps he could find a place in the tail of a man of standing and generosity: collops of venison and bramble jelly, amber uisge beatha in the glass; and after, time for the harp and the pipes; clarseach and pibroch. Then poems and the crowd listening in silence, hanging on the growing force of his utterance which breaks like surf across the long table. Silence then, as the guests sit and ponder until the fire crackles and they laugh together.

Or perhaps to Spain, where the princes fled – they who walk in sunlight and never want for fine clothes, or comfort, or songs among the fountains. Only poetry they do not have, poems of their lands and the people they have deserted. He could give them a draught of verses.

'Why stir yourself to these strange thoughts?' The woman has come. She is lying by his side.

Now follows the pillow talk between them.

'I have no lodging.'

'You are mine, my poet, my love.'

'You have bled me like a leech on the thigh of a wader.'

'Oh my own! You are handsome and tall, like an oak that was never cut.'

'I have no family, no master. I sleep in the crags.'

'Poet, your tongue is a silver path in the morning.'

'Go. You have blighted my flesh. I am a creel of air.'

'Poet, you have conjured me, so that I will see the noon again and feel the sun.'

'You have drunk the soul of me.'

'Poet, my love, you have given me life.'

'You have given me death.'

His eyes close. His mouth sags. All around is dark, save for the glistening slabs and jutting sharps. The woman reaches out her cool arm and cradles his head. 'Ochon, my love, my poet of gifts and wonders. Wake you again and tell me your verse.'

The bard shudders. His split lips grasp for words. At last he whispers, 'Go.'

'No.' She is shaking him gently, pulling at his shirt like a child waking an old man. 'Come, my boy, my golden boy, give.'

'Go.'

'Tell me again of my hair, my breasts.' Her slight fingers trace the creases of his cheeks.

'Your breasts?' He tries to raise an arm, but it falls.

'Yes.'

'Your breasts are like nubs on the poll of a faun ...' He stutters and gasps.

> 'Your voice was the curlew in search of the flock.
> Come, I have kissed your four limbs.
> Your skin was as cool as the mist in Ard Raithin
> Where the white cows wake
> And walk to the milking ...
>
> We ... we will run, you and I,
> In May when the tides are calm
> In a currach with two oarsmen ...'

'Yes.' Her face is close to his. Her eyes are pricked with fierce joy.

> 'To Scotland, the islands, where they welcome the poets.
> Or perhaps to Spain,
> Where the sons of the Gael walk
> In the summer gardens of Cordoba ... Perhaps ...'

'Yes?'

If we stay and wait in the glen, we will see the dawn come up over the corpse of a man so drawn and famished it is a wonder that he was able to climb so high among the boulders. We see him lying where no one will ever find his bones and a woman sitting near him. Her dress is the colour of laurel leaves. Her face has the look of a cat that has played too long with a small bird and is watching to see if it will move again. There are no tears in her eyes when at last she rises and disappears over the rim of the rocks.

145

The Headless Coachman

*T*he old bones of these islands clatter. I have heard it said that nowhere on earth is as haunted. There are spectral highwaymen who move from under dripping ash trees at midnight, the buttons of their coats twinkling like little stars. Their faces are masked and hidden. There are flimsy-limbed girls who drift moaning towards cliffs or quick flowing water; the reason of their original suicides long forgotten. There are old inns and grand homes where distant babies cry, yet you know there is no living baby behind the panels. Or chuckling lovers – in the next chamber which you know full well to be empty. Fox shriek on clear silver nights sounds like scratching despair. Are you sure it is not the split voice of a maddened woman whose suitor abandoned her centuries ago?

My grandfather told me of a ghostly carriage in Kildare, complete with a headless coachman and six galloping horses that breathed fire. To the lightning crack of a whip and the rattle of wheels the carriage would bowl up the road that led to the blind and ruined big house. Poachers and drunken late-night laggards unlucky enough to witness this spectacle would turn and run across the dark rain-tousled fields. Policemen leapt from their bicycles and threw themselves into ditches at the first warning of the rattling team.

The clench of their fear was that the carriage might be pulled up to a halt, the horses screaming and rearing, the sawn neck of the driver turning towards the quaking bystander. The door might open and voices summon the man to climb aboard and ride to a terrible midnight tryst in the halls of the crumbling mansion.

The Changeling

*T*he baby is crying. Downstairs there is music – Freddie and the Dreamers' You Belong to Me. Moira straightens from scrubbing the kitchen floor. She rubs her back, then holds the edge of the sink and looks out of the window. The view opposite is another kitchen. The face looking back at her is that of a West Indian woman of about her own age. Moira thinks the black woman has probably also been washing the floor. She almost waves at the woman but doesn't. Neither of them catches the other's eye. They look away on purpose.

It is 1965; three floors up in a sharp new council block. Lucky to get it, Desmond often says. He works for the gas board, digging up the roads at night.

A year ago and newly married they stepped ashore at Liverpool. They had a newly laundered look about them, like two fresh sheets pegged out on a line. They caught the train to Paddington. London was swinging. A clatter of Mods on red and blue burnished scooters snarled in a phalanx down Regent Street. Girls riding pillion in shiny black raincoats clung to their boyfriends. Moira and Desmond were scarcely twenty, but among the London youth you would have thought they came from a different generation. Desmond's suit had a loose country-cut look about it. Moira wore a green tweed jacket with a brooch in the lapel. Her mother had pinned it there at the bus station in Tralee; a tiny wrought figure of the Blessed Virgin. It was a Saturday in May. Around Piccadilly girls in white patent boots ran to meet boys in Paisley shirts. Desmond and Moira passed through the immaculate crowd, shy and invisible.

The baby is crying. Once, when she was a girl, a fox had caught its foot in the wire of the chicken coop. It screeched all night. The baby is building itself up to the same tawny wail. It puts Moira at the end of a dark tunnel of misery. The person downstairs turns the radio up. The Hollies' I'm Alive beats through the spaces each time the baby pauses for breath. Yet the shrieking continues and Moira fills the kettle with trembling fingers, her back turned to the door that leads to the hallway and the baby's room. He was born on the exact chime of nine months after their wedding day. That midsummer night, when the guests had all gone, the two of them left her mother's house as quiet as two towels slipping from a rail. Their shadows loped ahead of them down the boreen, as long as a pair of coupled greyhounds.

There was a ráth in a field where the bachelor Ahern kept three piebald ponies.

'Let's go up there' Desmond said, leading his new wife by the hand. 'We can watch the last of the sun go down behind Carrantuohill.' Moira said nothing, but her eyes in the strange late light of Beltain were like two smudging, dark anemones. They lay down among a flock of daisies and tall cow parsley.

Afterwards, when they were breathless and sweat-shrouded, the night was as still as ashes in a grate. The only sound was the champ and velvet shudder of the sleeping ponies. And for just one inkling Moira thought she heard the clinking of a tiny bell – a silver one, like a Sanctus that is rung in the mass. But the ring of this bell sounded very far away, faraway.

The baby is wailing. A pulsing and tearing cry it gives, red throated, to the morning – all anger and agony.

Such green eyes her baby has, such dark curls; eyes the colour of fresh weed in a stream, such white skin. When the nurse gave him to her she was faint from the birth, but his little hand reached for her cheek and she nearly swooned into her pillow with love for her new boy. The nurse smiled at her, looking a little puzzled as the baby felt for Moira's face. Then Desmond came in and they stared into the green eyes. The green eyes stared back. They had already decided that if it was a boy he would be given the name of Desmond's little brother Thomas, who had died when he was barely a day old.

The first time they had taken the baby to church he had given up such a caterwaul that they now took turns going to Mass without him. Moira took to stealing in at the back and when she went up to receive she was too nervous to look Father Toban in the eye. She left right away at the end of each service, embarrassed, in case the Priest asked her about dates for the Christening.

The air is blue with diesel fumes. She has wound her baby three times around in a pale blue knitted blanket. He is silent, even amidst the clatter and revving of Victoria Coach Station. Whole families are stowing themselves onboard for the journey. Homebound navvies are everywhere: white shirt, black trousers, donkey jacket. Bottles of stout, a pair in each pocket, swing like six-guns as they heave themselves up the throbbing steps. The baby sleeps on the coach. She holds him, face pressed to her breast.

A woman from Roscommon sits next to her all the way to Fishguard. She chitters like a sparrow. They pass through Luton, Birmingham and Cardiff, picking up more passengers. The woman asks about the baby. She is going home for the funeral of her brother.

'Terrible prices for coal this winter. Desperate weather. But isn't a baby a wonderful miracle? Will I hold him for you? No? Oh he's still sleeping. He's a great one for sleeping. Must be wonderful for you, with him such a quiet baby.'

Mrs Cooper the greengrocer's wife made a fuss of Thomas. She did her best to sieve most of the earth from the potatoes before she tumbled them into Moira's bag. Her glasses had spiky angles. Her wrinkled lips were thick with crimson lipstick. Ordinarily, she did not speak much to customers. She could hardly get a word in under Mr. Cooper shouting about carrots and cabbages at four pence so and so. One thing Mrs Cooper loved was children.

That Monday morning Moira was at the back of the shop with big, bald Mr. Cooper. She had asked him for some beetroot, but when he put them in the brown paper bag it split, spilling them on the floor.

'Sorry Love. I only just got them out of the kettle and they're still too warm see.'

Mr. Cooper scrambled for the beetroot and held them steaming over Moira's bag, his hands stained, as if with wine and blood.

Mrs Cooper's one regret about the shop was that her hands 'is always too dirty from grubbing in the bins all day to hold the little ones what come into the shop. And your little Thomas, look at him in his nice clean rompers. He's as fresh as a June picnic and you're a credit to him love.'

Lately Mrs Cooper had taken to standing with the pram while Moira went in to get what she wanted. If the baby was asleep she rocked the pram gently and chatted to the other women who stood by the fruit. If he was awake she selected the yellowest of bananas and held it up for him, saying, 'This is for your mummy to mash up for your tea. Yes it is. Yes it is. Coo.' However, that Monday, as Moira returned to the pram, she was struck by Mrs Cooper's expression. She was white in the face and her lipsticked mouth was as tight as the red seam along a postman's trousers. Thomas was awake, flexing his little fingers and laughing in the wordless joy of babies when they think something is absolutely hilarious.

'Well,' huffed Mrs Cooper, standing with her hands on her hips, her chest thrust up like the front of a London bus. 'I don't know how you did it, him being so young and all, but you never ought to have done it. Teaching him disgusting words like that? It's a crime. That's what I say. And what's more he screwed his little face up so ugly too. I should take him straight home right now my girl

156

and think about what you've done. Disgusting! Worse than the meat porters outside the Fletcher's arms. And he such a tiny thing.'

Moira opened her mouth but no reply came.

She tried again, 'I ... I don't ... Mrs Cooper ...' she stammered, but white shock wiped away the words from her tongue. She shifted her bag into the crook of her arm and pushed the pram. There were three women on the pavement and they parted as she went off down to the corner.

'Bloody Irish' one of them said as she passed. Tears needled the corners of her eyes. She felt as if she had been slapped in the mouth. Thomas laughed all the way home.

On the ferry many people sleep but some passengers drink through the night voyage in little groups. A man with a red quiff is singing The Star of the County Down –

    '... like a foolish elf, sure I shook meself
    Just to make sure I was all there'

It is a calm crossing. The baby does not stir. His breathing is the shush of a distant wind. The boat rocks gently and five fingers of spilt beer run across the deck towards Moira's feet.

Dawn over Rosslare is as bright as a knife-grinder's smile. The streets are wet and Moira is on another bus, pulling away from the coast. It is a day of many stops and rain is coming in rags across tattered fields. Moira feels the tiredness fumble at her eyes so she begins to suck sherbet drops hoping that the sharp lemon tang will keep her awake. The roads are rough but Moira welcomes each jolt and tip because that also keeps her from dozing. All the while the baby's breathing is as quiet as a rabbit's sigh in a warm hutch.

At the National School Miss Curran had taught Moira history. Those were long hours, when names and dates hummed over her. She often found herself becoming lost in the green glass of the

157

teacher's necklace. Twenty-six small beads and one large one cut with angles, so that it flashed, even in the dreary days. This was the way of it with her baby's eyes. He was either crowling with rage, or as silent and watchful as a heron in a pond.

There were many such hours in the flat. Moira would approach Thomas and look into his green deeps. She would feel the colour draining from her body. After a while she became nothing more than an echo in the white room. The baby still and keen; the mother struck in the fixed hold of the small child. Then suddenly he would jolt in his cot and jerk into a fury. Each time this happened Moira shuddered, drew back and went to weep in the kitchen.

On Wednesday morning, as Desmond lay sleeping, Moira walked the baby around the park after the rain. On returning she opened the door quietly. She left the pram in the corridor for a moment while she fetched an old towel so that the wet wheels would not sully the newly scrubbed floor. She pulled the pram inside but as soon as the door was closed three sharp knocks called her back to open it.

Mr. Baczowski stood there in his RAF blazer. His accent was like the clatter of a machine gun. He had a bright red burn scar all across his left cheek and down his neck. He was one of the few tenants who ever spoke to her.

Mr. Baczowski once told her how he had shot down six Nazi planes and how he came to get his scar. 'Vrooom -tacka -tacka -tacka! Bullets in the fuel tank. I bailed out, half my face gone. Ha!' He then spread his wings and vroomed off towards his own door.

But this morning Mr. Baczowski was clearly agitated.

'Terrible,' he said. Moira felt a hot rush in her chest. 'Your child whisper me bad words. Just now he whisper me.'

'He can't speak, Mr. Baczowski. He's too young.'

'Never I hear words from a child like this,' he stammered. 'Whisper, whisper. I saw many things in my life, but this? No. Diabla!'

158

'Mr. Baczowski, I ...' But he was already walking away, stiff and straight, his umbrella tap tapping.

The commotion woke Desmond. He came with dazed cork-screwed hair into the sitting room where Moira sat holding Thomas up in front of her. Tears blotted her mascara. The baby was laughing away like a chuckling spring.

She told Desmond. She told him about Mrs Cooper at the greengrocers. Desmond, in his quiet country way, explained to her that people in London had it against the Irish and would say anything. Sure, didn't he have to put up with jibes from the other men on the night shifts? Moira said that Mr. Baczowski was Polish and went to mass the same as them, so why would he say anything bad that wasn't true?

Desmond couldn't say, but he added with a directness he had never shown before, 'Moira I'm tired and should be sleeping for I have to be bright for work tonight. And it's you who should be keeping the baby quiet. He's always crying. Take him to the doctor or something'. Moira felt the lash of this, their first quarrel. She said nothing but placed Thomas back into his cot.

Dr. Bailey had very large hands and smoked a pipe.

'He's a little tinker right enough. He'll have you running up the walls by the time he's three, Mrs Cantillon. I wouldn't worry about his fits of temper and the crying. He's just a scamp demanding your attention. I can't find anything wrong with him.'

Moira held a tissue crushed in her two hands. Dr. Bailey was bouncing Thomas on his knee and he laughed when the baby made a grab for his pipe.

'It's your first child and you're far from home. And you're young yourself. He's probably picking up your anxiety. Just relax, Mrs Cantillon, and I'm sure he'll calm down too. Nothing to worry about.'

Dr. Bailey handed Thomas to her and opened the door. Moira stopped half way out.

'But, Doctor, some people say he's ...'

'Nothing to worry about, Mrs Cantillon.' Dr. Bailey was bluff in his tweeds. 'Go home now and enjoy him.'

On the bus Thomas was quiet and observant. His dark hair was growing into fine curls. Moira calmed herself with the doctor's kind, brusque authority. He must be right, she thought. She had been worrying about nothing.

In the flat the afternoon light was lemony across the sitting room wall. She fed the baby his rusks as the Beatles chorused Twist and Shout from the radio. Thomas was as good as gold. Moira sneezed and then discovered she had something in her eye. She left the boy in his high chair and went to the mirror over the fireplace. She held her eyelid up and tried in vain to spot the grit or whatever it was that was scratching her. For the tiniest second she stopped and looked at the reflection of the baby over her shoulder. For the tiniest second what she saw there was not a baby at all but a leering, wizened creature. It was kicking against the seat and tray of the chair and making the most crudely obscene gestures with its little claws. A voice like a rusty hinge crept up the skin of her neck – words of filth and blasphemy.

Moira turned in dread but now as she looked all she saw was the baby Thomas laughing at her with his green eyes as merry as flaming holly leaves.

At two in the afternoon the bus comes through the little town. Hurling pennants have been strung across the streets in the Kerry colours. Moira recognises two of the young men standing outside Casey's pub. She huddles down and looks away. In a moment they are out of the town and then driving the last stretch of country before the crossroads. Beyond the fields the mountains glint with eyries of light.

A half mile walk along a lane coiled with brambles. Moira climbs up into a field on a path that takes her away from her mother's home. The baby began to stir half an hour ago. His tiny fists screwed at his eyes. By the time she climbed down from the bus he was screeching, his green eyes baleful, his face red as if with a fever. As Moira walks away he reaches his hand over her shoulder towards the bus.

Her mother must not know she is back. Beyond the field where the bachelor Ahern keeps three ponies and where the ráth is grown over with cow parsley is a small hollow, little bigger than a steep ditch. In the daylight only the pale grey waft of turf smoke shows that a house is there. At night you might see the flicker of a yellow glow down there as if a giant is trying to light his pipe.

This is the house of Ellen Grey. She is past her ninetieth year but she has forgotten her exact age and there is none left alive who can tell her. Ellen lives on nettle stews and bread she bakes each day on a griddle over the fire. She has one tooth in her mouth. Her coat is sewn over with many patches. Shakespeare would recognise this old biddy; he knew three of her sisters.

The three piebald ponies stand staring into nothing as Moira walks across the field in her zipped-up London boots. Thomas wriggles and bucks and makes clumsy little slaps at her face.

Back in London Desmond will have found Moira's letter: 'I am using the money we were saving for Christmas. I don't know what else to do other than take him …' Desmond will also have found the sleeping tablets that Dr Bailey had given him when he had had trouble adapting to the night shift. On the kitchen table one of them lies chipped into small fragments. Desmond sits with the letter and looks at the tablets with a wrinkled brow.

He does not know that Moira has drugged her baby's milk or how sorely she has wept for it. He does not know her gnawing doubts, her clenched stomach, her heart yammering with guilt that she might kill the child with the tablets – that what she has seen might be no more than her own madness.

Ellen Grey stands in her doorway feeding her chickens. They scatter when Moira walks down the bank. Ellen Grey can give you a poultice for the toothache or for your nightmares. She knows the herb that will twine an unwanted baby from your belly. She uses a stick because she is so bent with arthritis. She peers at the visitor through a pair of murky spectacles. 'Is it you, Moira MacFineen?' she asks, using the girl's maiden name. Moira replies with country courtesy, 'It is, Ellen, and God save you.'

The tea from Ellen Grey's pot is a sharp liquor brewed from brown bog water and rusty leaves. Moira tells her story with Thomas ranting at her feet. Ellen collects firewood in a woven willow basket and it is into this she has placed the boy amongst the folds of his mother's tweed jacket. The basket creaks and shakes but after a while, and especially when Ellen looks into his eyes, the watchful quietness comes over him. The old woman's voice is itself like creaking wicker and she has a way of talking that is more like pronouncement than conversation.

'I have not seen this before in all my long years but I know what it is from what you do be telling me and from the stories told to me by my own mother, who lived in this house all her days, God rest her.'

Here Ellen Grey pauses and blows her nose upon her fingers. She flicks the snot into the embers of her fire.

'I have come across the sea in terrible desperation,' says Moira, the tears coming to her eyes again.

Ellen holds her hand up.

'Hush, girl, and listen while I give you the way of it.'

The old woman stands slowly, her stick tapping towards the baby.

'Now then, it is almost always vexed. It cannot abide the Holy Church.' She seems almost to be speaking to herself as she reaches to the mantle shelf high above the fire. 'And I can see with my own two eyes how oddly watchful it is.' With sudden deft agility Ellen bends and lays something black against the baby's cheek. The effect is mighty. A cry like a scorched cat breaks from the boy. Moira reaches for him, only to be poked back into her chair by the point of the stick.

'Leave him!' the old woman wheezes. 'First hold your hand out and then look at his face.'

Moira does as she is told. Ellen drops a sharp and cold metal object into her palm. It is an arrowhead and a welt in the exact shape of it is now rising on the cheek of her son.

'What have you done?' cries Moira with a breaking alarm in her voice. She pushes the stick away and scoops the boy up. He is livid. Froth gathers in the corners of his mouth. The arrow shape is like a brand on him. 'It is not your son!' Ellen brings her stick down hard on the flagstones.

'This is old iron. I found it in the field beyond. An arrow used by Finn mac Cumhaill, I shouldn't wonder, that was in Ireland before the English came. The Daoine maithe cannot abide iron. They cannot bear the Holy Water, but I have none. Anyway, there is the proof now. It is not your son.'

'What do you mean?' Thomas is hot and writhes in her arms. Once, Moira's father had taken her out to the river and they had caught eels. It was a hot day and they put the eels in a sack. For a joke he had made her hold the sack and it had twisted in just such a way as Moira's baby moved against her now. 'I gave birth to him. I have never been parted from him for an instant.'

'They are cunning. Who is it can explain their devilment? Sit back now and let him quieten. This is a thing that is very difficult to tell a mother, let alone have her act upon the knowledge of it. However, and only if you wish it, I will tell you, Moira MacFineen, what is in my mind regarding the child. And never mind the little thing lying there and all its caioneadh.'

'Tell me.'

'It is my certainty that the Good People have taken your son. Now, I know there are few people in these times who would support my thinking but it is the World that do be wrong in their forgetfulness of the ways of the Sidh. They have not forgotten. Nor have they given up their antics ...' And in the little thatched house at the back of the fields in 1965 Ellen Grey tells the pale young mother about how the Good People of the hidden kingdom have reached out from their ráth to lay an enchantment. The chickens pick in at the kitchen door and the baby kicks and wracks in the basket. She tells Moira how the people of the ráths will sometimes take a child and leave a creature in its place which they cover with a glamour so that it is almost impossible to see the truth of their mischief.

'It is nothing, Moira, but a broken thing of their own they have given to you. The longer it stays with you, the more it will sour your life for it needs the sap of your vitality.'

Ellen takes down a jagged piece of mirrored glass, spits on it and then rubs it with her elbow.

'Here, see it again for what it is, just as you saw it in your houseen in London.'

She holds the mirror over the baby and they both look to see a queer, yellow thing like an ancient naked man cast tiny in the basket. 'Listen,' said Ellen.

The little limbs flex and the cracked mouth opens.

An old, dry, cold voice comes to their ears, saying 'Mammy, Mammy! Feed me Mammy'.

Then the creature shrugs, laughs its rusty laugh and leers at them.

It is near to midnight on a ráth in Kerry in 1965. The cow parsley is damp and trodden down. An old woman stoops in front of the moon stoking a small fire of kindling and turfs. In the fire is an iron poker, dull red in the darkness like a dragon's tongue. To the side of the fire a baby frets.

'We could have boiled water to scald it in the kitchen. Or we could have tricked the thing to reveal itself further. But, by the Holy Powers, I am thinking it is better up here where they cannot mistake our intentions.' Ellen takes up the poker by its cold end.

'Not ready,' she says. 'Not yet.'

Moira is numbed. She is sure that Desmond will have telephoned the presbytery at the crossroads. Right now Father Cleary's housekeeper might be cycling down to her mother's house just a few fields away. She imagines Desmond in a London phone box with buses and motorbikes rushing past, and him not having the least idea of the madness she is entering here on the ráth. Fairies? No, not fairies – the Good People of the hills. Children stolen and

164

taken into the hollow lands?

Moira shivers and watches as Ellen reaches for the poker again.

'Now, girl, it comes towards the right colour, look.' The old woman brandishes the metal. It is a red wand. A piece of grass clings to it for a second before bursting to flame. Ellen smiles and Moira thinks that the old biddy is enjoying herself.

'Stop!' Moira kneels and clutches at the side of the basket. 'We will not do this. There must be something else. Another doctor or something.'

The baby is crying again, just like an injured fox, but his pudgy arms are reaching for his mother.

'There is no other way,' hisses Ellen.

'No. I will not believe in those old pishogues you speak of.' Moira goes to scoop up the basket but the old woman knocks her backwards into the grass.

'Enough of that! You have seen. And was it not you who heard a bell rung while you were at your play with Desmond Cantillon here on the hill? Ah, the ways of the young.' The poker is so close to Moira's face she can hear it fizzing in the evening breeze.

'Now. On my life, I will plunge this red iron down the throat of the brazen interloper and send it back to them.'

'No!'

Things happen very slowly. Ellen grimaces, then cries out as her hand is prised open and the poker is flung away over Moira's head. The old woman feels for her spangled arm, which now hangs limp. Moira is half up off the grass. A flaring wind hoists among the branches and thistles. She sees the rising shapes of people, silver and tall. Three - no - five, in number. They step from the grass in a confusion of colours and outlines, like a stained glass window brought to life in the moment of its breaking. Here a head, here an arm. Here a body whose head is lost. Voices come. Their words are all pitched together and laid over each other like beech leaves falling into a flooded gutter. Or glass smashing on flagstones. Or silver forks dropped into a sink.

One among them, a woman, comes, making herself whole as she treads the night grass. Her white arms are long in the moonlight. Her hair sweeps away the stars. Her mouth is as cold as a frosted rowan berry. She looks down at Moira. Her hand unfolds and her dark eyes roll into her head. She speaks. The words are like the gossip of branches in a deep wood; distant, unintelligible, yet there is a haughty command in them.

Moira flinches. She gropes for the baby but a rush of air and the sound of gulls kying around her in a flock of worry bewilder her, so she draws back her hand. She looks at the basket and there, in the flourish of light, is the little yellow creature revealed. It is flinching and laughing in silent derision. There comes a sound like two great lozenges of stone crashing together. Then nothing.

Moira realises that she is shivering; trembling and shivering as if she has awoken to a room in which the fire has died. She sees Ellen Grey standing above her but the glittering people have gone. Moira crawls to the basket and what does she see? Not the old, twisted thing but Thomas, her Thomas, her pure baby boy, sleeping peacefully in the moonlight.

Moira carried Thomas back to London. He never screeched again. Ellen Grey's arm hung useless at her side for the rest of her days.

Math son of Mathonwy

168

*I*t was back in the time in Britain when there were many rulers. One of them was Math son of Mathonwy who held numerous cantrefs in the old lands of Gwynedd. He was a fierce king and a powerful sorcerer. He had a wand so ancient that the wood was nameless to the race of men.

His shoulders were broader than the widest horn-span of a bull. His voice was like the bellow of a bull and his auburn hair grew thick into his great beard. This was the way they made the kings in Wales long ago.

Math son of Mathonwy was a restless man and could only bear the peacetime life at his court in Arfon if he had a lap-virgin always on hand who would hold his feet at all times and comfort him to tranquillity. In battle he was ruthless and mighty. However, when in his fortress Math spent his time feasting and dispensing hard, fair justice, with his feet up.

Now of the raid to which he was called to leave Arfon I will not tell, since I have to cut the cloth of the story to fit the pages. Save to say that Math son of Mathonwy was lured away by his two nephews to plunder some pigs from another king. He left his beloved lap-virgin Goewin alone with her ladies. Each day she looked out across the stone bordered fields and uncleared forests, awaiting his return.

These two nephews were called Gilfaethwy and Gwydion. Young and rangy, like two unbroken moorland colts they were, with a kind of jumpy wildness in their eyes. They took their uncle off on a bloody rampage across the little stone bridges, down the hidden trackways and over the moody mountains to the kingdom of Dyfed.

It was the return that showed the stark and wicked natures of these two lordlings. For Gilfaethwy's thoughts had long been blowing on the embers of a kindled lust for his uncle's lap-virgin Goewin. Together they had contrived the whole campaign, which ended in nothing more than futile slaughter. Such is the way of youth. Nevertheless, the nephews arrived back at Arfon unwashed, the day before their uncle Math son of Mathonwy. The stink of blood was on their furs, on their faces and on the poles of their spears.

Gilfaethwy dismounted in the muddy courtyard and ran to the chamber where Goewin was keeping lookout. Bursting in, Gilfaethwy and Gwydion beat the screaming women out of the room with the flat tangs of their stained swords. All except for Goewin. Gilfaethwy shrove the robes of the lap-virgin with a single tear of his hands. He threw her naked on the bed and together both nephews raped Goewin, whose screams were joined by the women locked outside. We will turn our faces away from the terror of this scene until the next morning...

...When Math son of Mathonwy rode into his fortress tired from his journey.

He tethered his horse. Then he washed and he oiled his auburn beard. He was so weary that he did not notice the women standing by in the shadows, slowly wringing their hands. At last, his ablutions done, he called for Goewin, so that he could rest his feet.

She approached him as pale and cold as melt-water in March. She could not meet his gaze and her shoulders shivered. She spoke in coughing sighs and told him she could not lay her lap open for his comfort. 'Lord, you must look for another virgin. I am now a woman.'

The eyes of Math son of Mathonwy were amber and his fury glowed in them steady and clear. With one great fist he drew her close to him and demanded why she had betrayed his trust. Goewin's anguish broke before him like a dropped clay vessel. 'It was your sister's sons lord. They dishonoured both you and me for they raped me on your bed. I was not silent. The women and the guards heard everything.'

Math threw his arms wide and bellowed like a bull for the two youths. They came to him from the where they had been skulking in far corners of the fortress. Halting, furtive and cringing they confessed their crime, as Math stood over them, dark as the peak of Mynnydd Mawr when it blocks sunlight from the pastures. At last he took Goewin's small hand in his own and told the whole court that he would marry her to restore her honour and give her power across all his cantrefs.

If Gilfaethwy and Gwydion thought there was an end to it all they were mistaken. For next Math son of Mythonwy drew forth the wand of ancient nameless wood. When he spoke it was like rocks rolling down the face of Mynnydd Mawr. 'You have been as beasts and beasts you shall become.'

He struck his dark wand on Gilfaethwy's head. 'Here,' he said. 'You shall go into a stag.' And there, an antlered red stag stood in front of him in the place of the first nephew.

He then seized Gwydion and clouted him with the wand. 'And you,' he said. 'You shall go into a hind.' At once a meek, light stepping, red hind stood next to the stag.

'Since you have been a pair in this crime I will send you off as a pair. You shall run into the wild forest and you shall breed as beasts.' Math's anger was slow but sure. 'Go now and return in a year.'

The stag and the hind went off and ate the young leaves and rutted in the glades far from men.

When the next spring came there was a morning when the guards set up a great clamour on the walls of the fortress. The dogs all sprang up barking and howling. Math son of Mathonwy was distressed. For a year he had had no lap-virgin to soothe him. 'What is it?' He cried.

A young man ran outside and then returned breathless. 'My lord there is a stag and a hind coming to the gates, with a young fawn stepping behind the two.'

Math rose and threw on his cloak. His beard was wild. He stood in the gateway, like a tree blocking the way. 'Bring me that fawn,' he said, with a voice like logs rolled across cobbles. He raised his black wand. The young fawn became a boy with auburn hair. 'I will call him Hyddwn and I will foster him to a wealthy man. You will never see your son again.'

Math walked out from under the arch of his gates. 'You who have been a hind and have known the thrusting of your stag mate - you will go into a wild boar. And you who have been a stag and thrust against your hind - you will go into a wild sow.' Sure enough, when Math son of Mathonwy lowered his wand there stood a black-coated and tusked boar next to a chestnut-coloured sow.

'Away now' he said, 'Into the far places and breed together. Come back in a year.'

The boar and the sow ran off into the trees. They snouted for worms and coupled in muddy wallows.

On a morning the next spring Math son of Mythonwy was pacing in his chamber. He was pulling at his hair and fretting for he still had no lap-virgin to caress his feet and calm the fires in his blood. He paused when he heard all the dogs in the fortress suddenly breaking into a howling, barking chorus. Then he heard his men all rattling their shields and spears. Math went outside wearing only his shirt. His beard was wild. 'What now?' he asked.

'A large boar and a sow are trotting towards the walls lord,' replied one of his soldiers. 'And behind them is one striped piglet.'

Math ordered his gates to be opened. He stood under the lintel and his voice was like a tree falling across bracken. 'Fetch me that piglet.' It squealed and struggled but when Math laid his dark wand on its brow it became a sturdy boy with auburn hair. 'Well, I will take this boy and see that he is fostered to a generous man.' He turned to the boar and the sow. 'I will call him Hychdwn and you will never see him again.' There was a look almost of anguish in the eyes of the two animals. But if they thought their trial was at an end they were mistaken. 'As for you,' roared Math son of

172

Mathonwy, 'Stand still.' He walked out into the pasture and held his wand between them. 'Let me see...you who are a boar will go into a silver she-wolf. You who were a sow will go into a grey wolf.' In an instant they were transformed.

'Off now up into the mountains and breed with each other. Return to my walls in a year.' The two wolves loped quickly away to the heights where the forest does not climb.

In the crags and coombs the wolves hunted for hares. Under the full moon they yipped and trembled against each other in manner of mating dogs.

The next spring there came one bright morning when the fortress was quiet. All except for Math who was raging as if with a fever, for he still had no lap-virgin to be tender to his feet. However, he was distracted by the cries of his men on the battlements. Then all the dogs awoke and joined in, gnashing and leaping. The men rang their swords on their shields.

'What's up?' asked Math son of Mythonwy.

'I'll go and see.' replied the old man who was washing the floor. In a while he returned wheezing. 'Two wolves are waiting in the shadow of your walls lord. And with them is a grey wolf pup, running between their legs.'

Math son of Mathonwy took up his dark wand of nameless wood and hurried outside. He threw the open gates and stood in archway, tearing at his thick hair. His voice was like the crashing of a ship on sharp rocks. His beard was wild. 'So you have returned again. Guards fetch me that cub.' He touched the little wolf with his wand and it became a fair-faced boy with auburn hair. 'I have the name Bleiddwn ready for him. I will foster him to a wise man and you will never see him again.'

Math walked up and down in front of the slinking wolves. Then he raised his black wand again. 'The pair of you have wronged me and also Goewin who is dear to me, but you have served your sentence.' He struck each of them so that Gilfaethwy and Gwidion returned to their rightful bodies. Then he fixed them with

173

his amber stare. 'It is a terrible disgrace that each of you has had children by the other and you will carry that forever.' Math son of Mathonwy then called for the women to draw a bath. 'Wash their heads and dress them,' he said.

Arianrhod

*M*y name means silver wheel. My palace turns slowly in the great north sky. There was a time when my home was anchored to sharp rocks off the coast of Gwynedd. It was made all of wet slate and granite. Chains of white gulls circled my battlements. The salt rain was ever in my silver hair and my gown clung to me wetly, but I was happy there alone in the slick-flagged courtyard and on the spray-flecked ramparts. Now, when I recall the seal pups mewling on the reefs at low tide it brings me straightaway back to the son I lost to the waters and of another son who was set against me. The shame of their birth and the confusion of it now passes more quietly over my brow. I am beyond the years of men and my fury has cooled to become a pale ghost in the cloisters of my heart …

My palace is wrought all of stars. I wander the silver chambers and frosted halls. I am quiet now, and if not happy, I am content. There are no raw mornings or calm sunsets here. Only the palest glow casts across walls of smooth crystal. The breeze from distant galaxies plays through my silver hair. I turn slowly and I am forever alone.

For all that has been said of my own wickedness, there was none so wronged as me. Goewin the lap-virgin was disordered by my brother and yet for some reason it was I who dropped two sons in front of Math and his whole troop of retainers! Surely there was some sorcerous contrivance which drew me in, perhaps merely to give some grotesque symmetry to the whole story. I often wonder if it was Math himself, my father's brother, who orchestrated everything all along. After all, he placed his broad hand on the tousled heads of many boys and gave them their names. Almost as if he was an old jealous bull, intent on claiming all the new season calves for his own.

No doubt you have heard that when I went to Math's keep I was made to leap across his wand. And of the fair-headed son who sprang from between my legs at the very moment of stepping over? When I looked back I saw that I had also let fall a ball of flesh.

Anyway, suddenly shamed and hollow, and astonished with emptiness, because I had never known a man or known myself to be full, I ran back towards my tower above the rocks. There I griped for many days with a raw wind howling through my casement and the click-clawed crabs side-slanting across the floor. My tears were like silver minnows flashing amongst the flotsam of a spring night.

I was told one morning by a cockle woman that my firstborn had fled to the ocean as soon as he could walk. The name Math gave him was Dylan son of Ton, which holds all the ebb and flow of salt water in it, for it means nothing more or less than 'sea wave'. The old woman told me that my son went to live on the crests of the swells and in the green depths. Unexpected, unwanted – and so much missed – my boy who was lost to me from the instant of his first cry.

Of the bundle I had slipped as I headed for the door, the cockle woman knew nothing. I went back and stared at the sea sucking and heaving at the feet of my tower until I grew giddy with its rise and fall. In the pause between each wave surge I found myself pondering on what I had been before Gwydion had summoned me to the fortress of Math son of Mathonwy.

I found that I had no memory of that life. As new as a glass of fresh milk I had set out for Math's place that morning. It was as if I had stepped into the world with nothing behind me, except a love of my own company and a delight in the halls of my own sea-cradled towers. I knew that Gwydion and Gilfaethwy were my brothers, in the way that I recognised a grey cloud or the shadow of a tree, but they had been hitherto untold in my mind. In the same way, I knew Math son of Mathonwy was my uncle and that my father was the mighty Don whom I had never seen. How long had my existence been, before my brother's command came to leave my rain-slaked walls? Days? Years? Centuries? I had no idea. .

Now, mourning the void in my belly I sat rocking in time with the drag and rush of the silver-topped tides and I could have done so for the eternity left to me, until my palace was worn down by the water, until I forgot myself, and could be engulfed at last.

It was the sharp mobbing gulls' cries that stopped all this. For I also began to realise that I appear to be always the silver needle sewn into the story of men. Yet I carry no silken thread at my tail and so I do not hold the stories together. I flitter in through their purposes with about as much importance as a gull slanting across the heads of a band of shore-seeking sailors.

I lay on the soaked stone, alone, wrapped in tresses of dulse and kelp for a full-moon cycle of waxing and waning. My anger grew for these men-creatures, these thieves and tricksters, these lusty namers and governors. Like nacre like ancient lunar ice, accruing layer upon layer, my pitiless anger honed to a blade.

One blustery morning as I was eating laver and guillemot eggs I saw from my casement two figures walking the strand. One of them was Gwydion. I rose and left my grey halls and met them among the tussock grasses where salty sheep graze. With Gwydion was a tall youth with yellow hair.

'A year has passed since you came to Math's fortress,' said my brother.

'Has it?' was my reply. 'I know nothing of the time men keep.' Gwydion shrugged. 'We have come to find you.'

'Who is this boy who follows in your steps?' I asked.

'This is your son whom I have raised for these past four seasons.'

'How can that be?' I asked. 'He is nearly a man.'

'I took him when he was but a nub of flesh and saw to it that he was given the best in all nourishment,' replied Gwydion. 'He has grown quickly and is the marvel of Math's court. When he was only four months old it seemed as if four years had gone into him. At eight months he stood half my height and so on and so on, until I thought it best to bring him to you.'

I was dazzled by the sting of my own response. The blade of my tongue was unsheathed. 'What cruelty prompted you to show me this boy who is nothing more than a pang of my shame? Why do you delight in laying open the shell of my disgrace for the world to see?'

Gwydion placed his arm around the youth. 'There is no shame in loving this fine boy. I do, as if he were my own son. Arianrhod, you should love him too and wave your disgrace away on the wind.'

'What name do you call him?' My words glittered between us and I saw that Gwydion thought he had consoled me.

'As yet he has no name.' He replied.

'Well then,' I readied my tongue and pronounced a tynged over the boy's head. It was cold as moon silver, or a knife dropped into a bowl of ice water at midnight. A doom-spell. A tingling forged curse. 'He is a stain on me,' I cried. 'He is a thorn to my heart and he shall never have a name unless he obtains one from me.'

Gwydion drew back, as if I had struck him, saying 'These words are your real shame, sister. You have let your generosity wither because your virginity is lost. Yet, one way or another, the boy will take a name from you. This I swear.'

I turned from them and made for the gates of my palace. My mouth was numb from the sting of my first tynged.

In the chamber above the rocks I spent a month on the cold floor. The sea reached over the sill and threw dogfish purses, oarweed and barnacles across my silver dress. The gulls rode the grey sky and cried into the wind. I lay alone and grieved in the fathoms of night that washed up from the well where my two sons were hatched.

One morning I heard voices down below. I looked out and saw a small ship had sailed up to the strand from the direction of Caer Dathal. On the sand the old cockle woman was talking to the crew. There were two men, both brown and burly. The ship had a red sail that flapped and cracked even though the morning was calm. I called to the cockle woman. She came to my gates. I stood there with my dress glistening in the sunlight.

'Who are they?' I asked.

'Shoemakers,' the old woman replied. 'On their way to Aber Menai. They have hides of leather from Spain - red and tooled and painted with gold spirals – the finest I have ever seen.'

'I have gone barefoot for far too long. Measure my feet and tell them to make me some shoes and I will give them three pearls.' The cockle woman went to the cobblers. I could see that their hair was dark and curly. They wore the earrings and cloaks of Spain. They spoke the hoarse words of that country.

When the tide was sinking the cockle woman came to my gates with two new shoes in her basket. Straightaway I could see that they were too big.

'Take them back,' I said, looking out to where the shoemakers were standing on the deck. 'I will only pay them if they make them smaller.' The cockle woman walked away with the shoes.

When the tide was out and the ship was beached the cockle woman returned with two exquisite shoes so small they looked as though they had been made for a doll.

'What is this?' I asked. 'Why can't they make them the right size? I will not give pearls for this poor work.' The cockle woman went back with the shoes.

When the tide had risen and the ship was tugging against its anchor the cockle woman came to my gates. I stood in the archway with my silver hair fluttering out across my eyes.

'They wish you to go to them,' said the old woman. 'They say that they must see your white feet if they are to make you a pair of good shoes.'

I stepped across my threshold and went down to the ship. The two shoemakers were sitting cross-legged on the deck cutting patterns into the red leather hides. There was one older than the other. They smiled at me and hailed me in the hard accents of Spain.

181

I spoke to them.

'I am surprised that two craftsmen such as you could not make a pair of fitting shoes for me.'

The older one stood and leaned against the mast. 'Ah, now I can see the length of your feet,' he replied in a voice like a rusty gate, 'I will be able to gauge the exact measurements.'

Just then a wren flew in to rest on the prow. Quick as the gleam of a fish knife the younger cobbler flung a stone and caught the wren between the bone and the sinew of its leg.

'I have never seen the like of this,' I said. 'Your companion strikes with a skilful hand.'

'He does. He does,' agreed the older shoemaker. 'And it will prove a curse to you.' With that he waved his arm. The ship shuddered and collapsed to become a pile of kelp. From it stepped Gwydion and my son, now shorn of their disguise.

I drew back as if salt had been cast into my eyes.

Gwydion laughed. 'You have given the boy a good name. He will be known as Lleu Skilful Hand from now on.'

I pointed at Gwydion with the stab of my finger. 'Causing me this agony will not do you any good.' I let out a scream and spoke a tynged over the head of the youth. A curling, bitter curse, all split like ice in a pail. A frost-lick doom. 'I swear that the boy will never have weapons until I choose to arm him. He will be as useless as those shoes you made.'

I turned from them and went through my gates where they could not follow. This second tynged was like a cough of silver pins in my throat.

For a month I lay on the stone floor among the starfish and bladderwrack and green sea glass that the waves tossed in each night. Silver and cold were my half-dreams. In them I climbed inwards down the ladder of my own ribs and reached for the empty basin of my pelvis. Yet always I awoke with a start, as if I had been suddenly turned back at a walled frontier. As the dawn seeped in I webbed my hands around my waist questioning the secret trick-

182

ery that had sown the two seeds of my sons deep inside me. Why was I forbidden the answer?

When the summer was done there came a morning when the air changed. Birds of all kinds were being called south across the sea. There were silver clouds on the horizon.

I heard clear voices at my gates. I looked out to see two handsome young men with the long hair and fringed cloaks of bards. They commenced a song, matching each other line for line. No doors are closed to the bards. They are always welcome. I stood at the top of my staircase listening. I went down and stood in the close and listened. At last I spread my hands on the wooden doors, listening to them singing outside. The song was all about the legions who tramped the lands long ago and the clearing of the trees ...

Kindle lick the bark to flames
The oaks smoulder and blacken
Make a broad straight path
And pave it with white stones.

I found myself beckoned into the mesh of their glad voices. I reached for the bolts and drew them open. I called them in and led them to a hall that looked out over the bay.

I made a fire of driftwood in a hearth that had long been cold and empty. These handsome young men, both tall, but one more so, threw off their fringed cloaks and sat before it. I gave them a dinner of mackerel and kale and little griddle cakes. All the while they were singing and telling stories, one against the other. They had honey-coloured eyes.

It was a long night of words. More than had ever been known in my fortress. Laughter and lament – bards are bold acrobats in this art. They can make language turn somersault. So it was with this long-haired pair. When they told the stories from Ireland it was as if I could taste the rain and wind of that country. They spoke of a mountain in the kingdom of Connacht and I saw it

183

before me, grey and green – a wolf crag. They sang of a king slain in battle and I saw him bloody and pale, as if he lay right there between me and the bright hearth. I drank a flask of pale mead with my two visitors. They were the only guests ever to enter my fortress.

At last they grew weary and wrapped themselves in their cloaks. I left them to sleep in front of the embers. The night was calm. In my dreams I was a glassy elver drifting on the swell. My vexing had been hushed by the wash of the bards' singing and banter.

CLAMOUR! There had never been such an uproar in my halls. Voices bawling alarm out on the battlements. The sound of running feet on the stairs. The door of my chamber buckling under the hammer of fists.

'Lady, lady. Come to the walls!' Panic was in the eyes of my guests.

'What calls you to shatter the dawn like this?' I asked. I pushed away my silver hair, for it still had dreams caught in it.

'Look to your casement,' one of them cried. I turned to see the bay choked with a thousand scarlet sails.

'A fleet has come in the darkness,' added his companion. 'They are on either side of the causeway and their scaling ladders are poised.'

I went to the battlements and saw that it was true. A storming siege of men was poised to assail my towers. They were shouting their war cries. The morning sun licked across their helmets and picked on the points of their spears. My hands went to my mouth. I felt slender in the wind, like a single blade of corn. The gulls above me wheeled away to the west with despair in their beaks. 'What are we to do?' I asked, picking at the sleeve of my gown. Fear like a draught of icy water panged me. 'Have you weapons, lady?' cried one of the young men as he leaned out over the walls.

'Yes,' cried the other. 'We need arms to defend this place. Or we will all be slaughtered.'

I took them to a room in the highest turret. I opened the chests and showed them steel swords and tight-sprung bows. I showed them coats of silver mail, arrows too, with cold, dark points. The bards hefted the blades. 'Quick' I said. 'I will help you put on these trappings, for the baying of the army below is getting louder.' 'Him first,' said the tallest of the two. So I helped the other slide the mail over his head. Then I buckled his belt quickly and handed him a blue shield.

'Is it done?' asked the tallest, who had been looking out through a slit in wall.

'Yes,' I replied. 'And now you too must arm yourself.'

He turned to me. 'I have no need to put on these things now.'

'What?'

'Come, look here.' He drew me towards him. I saw that there were no soldiers at the ramparts and all the ships had gone.

'Where is the war band?' I asked, shocked and doubting what I had just seen. 'And what kind of host can depart so quickly?'

'This was a host to undo the last tynged you swore,' said the tallest bard. 'This boy has arms now from you. And no thanks to your wicked schemes.'

I reeled from his words. He passed his hand over his face and I saw instantly that he was Gwydion. I turned and saw my son also stood there in his new battle gear.

'This is harsh evil,' I hissed. 'The conjuring you have done against me will come to haunt you. It is against all custom that you have come into my halls disguised, where no man was ever before.' I put my arm up and summoned a tynged. A scratching curse it was, like the silver cry of a sea eagle. A chill, slicing oath. A fork of lightning saved in a buried crock. 'I swear from the deeps and dark of my heart that this boy will go unmarried, for he shall have no wife of the race of men.'

'You were always vengeful and bitter,' replied Gwydion. 'Yet I have undone all your schemes so far and Lleu here shall have a wife in spite of your spells.'

'Go!' I screamed at them. It was as if I was vomiting thorns at

185

them and here in my own place they had no power to stay. It was good, at least, to see them quail. They took off and I made the gates to my fortress slam behind them.

The last of my tynghedau was bitter as buckthorn berries on my tongue.

I lay on the floor of my chamber through a month of gales. When the sea slapped at my walls red urchins and razor shells were scattered over me. Clams rattled like beads in my silver hair. The water pooled around me. I slept and mourned the shoaling space inside me. It was like a grotto under the waves that I could grope for, yet never quite enter, as the lack of air made me surface.

I awoke one morning to find that the storms had passed and the air had been washed clean. I looked out of my casement and saw the white sand and clear water. I could see the fishes under the lip of the tide. My sight was silver in the dawn.

I went down to talk to the old cockle woman who was unstrapping a sieve and long rake from her back. 'A fine morning for your work,' I said as I drew near.

'That it is, my Lady,' she said, smiling, as she made her gear ready. 'Because of the storms I haven't been down to the shore of late. Many strong men have perished out there these last weeks.'

'That means nothing to me,' I replied.

She looked at me. Her eyes were blue and grey, like gull's feathers. 'No,' she said. 'I suppose not.' Her tone did not seem unkindly. 'I have heard of your three tynghedau and how the first and the second were undone.'

'What of the third?' I asked.

'I have news of that, my Lady.' She placed her tools down and took my hand. 'Come sit on this dune and I will tell you.' So the two of us went and sat and looked out to sea.

'I had occasion to walk near to the fortress of Math son of Mathonwy. The rain had been passing over me all day and so I went under the leaves by the forest path. As evening drew on there came a gap in the weather and for the first time in ages the clouds parted.

186

I was happy then for I could see my way through the trees. Now, I go quietly, so when I came upon two figures in a clearing I was able to step back into the darkness and watch what they were doing.

'One was Gwydion, your tall brother. The other was Math himself. He was stroking his great auburn beard. Together they were at some secret business. As the moon rose I saw them take flowers and lay them together. First they laid the green oak flowers. Then the yellow broom petals, and lastly the pure white meadowsweet. I kept this vigil while the moon rose. Math and Gwydion both muttered and sang quietly as they bent to their task.

At about midnight the scent of the flowers grew and the two men stood back. On the ground between them was the semblance of a girl all woven from petals. Math looked down at this curious effigy. "Come forth now," he said. The wind and the moon were stilled for an instant. The trees all stopped swaying. And there, all kissed silver in the moonlight, instead of the blossom form lay a living girl, opening her eyes and stretching as if waking from a long sleep. She stood between them and she was the loveliest girl I have ever seen, for in her beauty was the essence of flowers.

'Math held out his hand. "Your name will be Blodeuedd and we will take you away from this glade," he said. "And you will be a wife to Lleu Skilful Hand, the son of my nephew Gwydion."

'Then all three of them walked off towards Math's fortress with the girl going quietly in the middle and the scent of meadowsweet trailing after her.'

The old cockle woman smoothed her skirts. 'That is what I saw and heard, my lady.'

I laughed out loud. As far as I could recall it was the first laugh that ever broken from my lips. The cockle woman looked shocked. I clapped my hands together. 'They think they have been wily in conjuring up a bride made of flowers. They think that they have skirted around the doom I lay on my son.' I brushed my wet gown down and stood up from the dune. 'This mischief will play bad. For all their man-magic this just shows that my third tynged still holds.' I laughed again and bade farewell to the cockle woman.

'What will you do now?' She asked as she leant on her rake.

'You will see,' I replied. I walked towards my towers out on the causeway. The clear water reflected me as a flicker of silver. I locked my gates behind me and vowed that I would never open them again.

Lastly

Of the girl Blodeuedd I know nothing more. Nor did I ever discover why I suffered the bewilderment and disgrace of my pregnancy. Nor who plotted it. I admit to some pity for the girl made all of flowers – another woman called up from nowhere to suit the designs of men. Petals are of such flimsy substance. Perhaps she knew love and joy. However, I doubt it.

As for me, I unmoored my palace from the reef and the causeway, and let it drift away into the north sky, where it spins now slowly. I expect the old cockle woman spread the word of this retreat.

I am contented that the binding silver temper of my last tynged was too strong for my enemies. My silver hair flutters with starry dreams. My towers and my cloisters are quiet and I am alone.

Blodeuedd

*T*he owl has two cries, each one desolate and far-travelling. The first is a round hoot, an unseen sob, always beyond and away in the dark branches. The second is a shriek, near and sudden, an ear scraping rage that comes clawing from black corners where the moon does not look. All the other birds shun or mob the owl. Friendless and outcast it glides, like the scrap of a lonely lost dream through the night-silvered woods.

The owl is all the more remarkable for the fact that it was once a girl – and a beautiful girl at that, with garlands of wildflowers in her hair. And her dress all stitched from bright petals...

Math son of Mathonwy and Gwydion his nephew led the girl Blodeuedd to his fortress and gave her to Gwydion's son Lleu of the Skilful Hand. Fair headed Lleu had grown quickly to be a burly warrior. Strong as thick boiled leather, his skin had darkened in the summer sun. His features were blunt and golden.

Out in the green deep of the forest Math and Gwydion had laboured long with meadowsweet, oak flowers and broom - making the form of a girl on the forest floor. Math spoke words over the form that even he did not quite understand, for he got them from carvings on age-worn stones that he had found standing under the trees. Old words from old magicians long, long ago, who thrived before the sons of men came to these islands.

And when they finished speaking they stood back and watched as the figure shuddered to life. As the girl made of flowers sat up, Math felt a pang that they might have done something that should not have been done. Yet there was no other way to break Arianhrod's binding silver tynged, that Lleu could never have a mortal wife.

So, like a hand passing through a spring meadow, Blodeuedd the flower maiden, went to the marriage chamber and all the court were silent before her. She was lovely, they say, as cornflowers found among tall grasses. Her hair was red as a colt's mane. Her eyes were violet. The guards who stood outside the locked door pondered all night on how Lleu would be disrobing his bride, letting her sown petal gown fall to the floor, taking her to the bed. In whispers they pondered on the secrets of Blodeuedd's white limbs and small breasts that Lleu was enjoying, as they waited for the dawn to come.

When the grey light did break Lleu appeared at the door and told his men to saddle the horses. They looked over his shoulder they saw that his bride was sleeping. Her copper hair was laid out on the pillow, like the flames of Calan Mai.

'Gwydion has given me a strong castle in the cantrev of Dinoding,' said Lleu. 'It's there I will take my wife.'

At the head of his troop rode Lleu and the violet-eyed Blodeuedd. The fortress was called Mur Castell and there he loved his wife for two nights more, while the guards outside the chamber imagined her naked beneath him in the darkness.

Cock crow came after the second night in the fortress and Lleu went out to his retainers. He called on them to ready the horses, for they would ride out and survey the cantrev and then visit Math Son of Mathonwy away over the mountains.

What of Blodeuedd? The girl whose lips were scarlet flax. The girl whose skin was white as nettle flowers. The girl whose nipples were hawthorn berries. The girl whose wild stare was the colour of cats' eye sapphire.

With her words of love, like the wind hushing through a field of green corn she had twined with Lleu for three dark bed nights.

Her fingers had been leaf-touch on his cheek, his chest and his thighs. She was nimble and skilled in love making. After all, she was made for this purpose only.

Now she was left alone to sit gaze out at the peaks and trees, with no company at all.

On the third day of sitting the weather cleared after rain. Blodeuedd heard horns braying from the forest and then she saw a wounded boar break cover. A huntsman pursued the boar. His black horse kicked up sods as he chased the quarry from one stand of trees to another. Then came the rest of the hunt. They wore buskins and chequered cloaks. One of the footmen paused for a second on the green sward in front of the castle. They all seemed happy to be out in the fresh afternoon.

Blodeuedd called for the young servant boy who had been left behind to attend her. He came shuffling and blushing to her room. He could not meet her violet eyes. 'Go and find out the name of the huntsman on the black horse,' she said in a voice like slow bees in the brambles.

The tow-headed boy returned stuttering and picking at the threads on his shirt.

'Lady, it is Goronwy the Staunch, Lord of Penllyn. He has killed the boar and is busy feeding the tripes to his hounds.'

'That is a bold man,' replied Boldeuedd, 'to come chasing his quarry across our lands.' Her voice was the swish of rushes by a still lake. 'How many hours of daylight are left?'

'No more than one,' said the boy, looking at the floor. 'He is in a copse not far from our gates.'

'Well, we cannot let this Goronwy the Staunch stay out among the gorse and thorns. That would be a disgrace.' Blodeuedd stretched out her hand but the boy drew back, his face all flustered crimson. 'Go and ask him in,' she laughed.

The Lord of Penllyn stood square in the gateway. His cloak swirled around him in chequered greens and purple. His buskins were tight at his thighs. In his hands he held the fresh heart of the boar. Blodeuedd stretched out her arm to welcome him.

What shall I tell you of the dusk that came down in whispers about them, as the flames smacked and bristled in the grate? It was like a dark curtain swathing plushly around their shoulders. Blodeuedd unloosed Goronwy's cloak and let it fall. In a circle of candles she washed him down from the blood and dirt of the hunt. They ate a dinner of boar's heart and Spanish wine.

Across the table they held each other in their eyes so that neither could move until the candles burned low, leaving them still in the blackness. When the embers guttered low they stopped speaking. For three days and three nights Blodeuedd and Goronwy twined together in the bed. Her fingers locked across his back; his hips shuddering over the lily of her flesh. That was a long feast.

There are those who say the sweetest beds are those strewn with secret lust. Others hiss away from such thoughts, like spring leaves doused in salt. Whatever; Blodeuedd was made as she was. Her sole art was seduction. Goronwy, however, had ridden brazenly across Lleu's cantref. True, he had been beckoned in to the fortress, but he went eagerly. His glad eye was bright and he came tasty to the tryst.

On the third morning Goronwy the Staunch rose and stood before Blodeuedd. He was white-skinned in the light. His brown curls reached to his shoulders. 'I am away to my dogs and my men,' he said.

'You must not leave me,' replied Blodeuedd. The tears in her sapphire eyes took the glint of the fresh morning. 'Stay.'

Goronwy looked at her. 'I can be with you but there is only one way.' She was kneeling up on the bed. Her hair was like a red evening between trees in the deep woods. The nubs of her breasts were the red of mulberries. Her skin was like apple petals. 'We must learn how Lleu can be killed,' he said.

'Yes,' said Blodeuedd. Her voice was slow as thick mead poured into a stone cup. She lay back on her bed and slept. When she woke Goronwy was gone.

Lleu of the Skilful Hand returned and cast off his furs. Blodeuedd followed the pattern of her making as surely as a bluebell is called to flower by the sun. She washed the dirt and sweat of the ride from her husband's limbs and then led him to the bed. 'Tell me husband. They say you are stronger than the bear whose pelt you wear.' Her sapphire eyes gleamed in the fading light of the afternoon. 'Yet, still I am worried.'

'Why so?' asked Lleu. He stood framed in the arch of the open casement. The cool wind whicked across his wet skin.

'A fear has come on me,' she replied. 'I cannot name it yet.'

'In that case let me in enjoy you and worry in the morning,' said Lleu as he slipped between the blankets.

'Yes my love,' she said.

Lleu shook himself to the dawn and rose without a word. He hunched his broad shoulders into his shirt. Then he buckled his belt around his iron-mailed hips. When he looked up he was surprised to find his wife standing there before him and the door. There were five candles still flickering in the room. Blodeuedd trembled between the light of the guttering flames and the pale morning.

'What?' asked Lleu.

'Crows awake sometimes from dreaming and fly off through the branches, breaking themselves blindly in the darkness. This I know, although I do not know how I know.'

'Why give me this riddling?' Lleu eyed the door and sniffed the wind coming in from the casement.

'Because unlike the crows I have named the fear of my own dream.' Lleu was anxious to be away but Blodeuedd took his restless golden face in her slender fingers. 'My great fear is that you will die and that I will be left in this tower without you.'

Lleu laughed and sat down on the bed. 'It would be a hard job to kill me, for the magic of Math, my great uncle, has been spoken over my head.'

Blodeuedd's violet stare was like the sun coming through thick ice. 'Then tell me my love. For I believe that if I can hold the secret of your death then I will be able to keep you safe.'

'You keep me safe?' He laughed again. 'With your small white feet and your breath of mint, and your dress all made of petals?'

His blunt fingers passed over her breasts and down to her stomach. She was standing before him.

'Give me this secret, if nothing more than to give me peace.'

Lleu sighed. 'The horses are saddled in the yard. My men have eaten bread and are ready. I have another rough journey to make today. But to soothe you I will tell you how I can be killed, since the tynged is tightly sewn around me and I cannot see how anyone could break it.'

He held both her hands as he spoke. 'Whoever comes against me will have to bear a spear wrought in secret for a year in the hour before dawn - a dark, nameless spear, with barbs along the blade.'

'Are you sure?'

'I am. And what's more I cannot be killed under a roof, or under the sky. I cannot be killed on foot, or horseback.'

'Then how?' asked the girl.

'This is how it was told to me. Someone would have to bring a cauldron to a river bank, where the white stones lie. This someone would have to make a roof of thatch over the cauldron and set a fire underneath to heat the water and so give me a bath in the fresh spring air.'

'And then you could be killed?'

'No there's more. In order to climb from the cauldron, clean and sprightly, I would need to step first on the back of a pure white buck-goat brought down from the high mountains. And in the very poised instant, with one foot on the rim of the cauldron, and the other on the goat, whoever came against me then would have a chance of giving me death. So I have been told.'

Blodeuedd was joyful. 'Now this is such an intricate tynged, I see I have nothing to fear.' She kissed her husband and her lips tasted of blackcurrants. Then she stood aside as he went to his business.

As soon as he was away on the road she sent a message to Goronwy the Staunch and her violet eyes flashed happily.

Blodeuedd was often alone. Lleu was vigorous in ruling his cantrev. When he did return it was only for a night or two. He would bed his wife then sleep for ten hours before riding out again. Blodeuedd kept their lovemaking as fresh as cut lilies. She was skilled in this as no other, for this was her only purpose.

A year passed and there came the first day of spring. Blodeuedd sent a message for her husband to meet her on a riverbank where white stones lay. She had men from the fortress carry down an ancient silver cauldron, all beaten with the forms of animals. Then she made them thatch a good roof over the cauldron. Once this was finished she filled it with fresh water and kindled a fire of dry twigs underneath. She told the men to leave and she waited for Lleu.

She was standing by the bath house when her husband rode down the valley to the waterside. He was smirched with the mud and sweat of his journey.

Blodeuedd was dressed in her gown of flowers and there were snowdrops in her red hair. She smiled to see Lleu on his horse, picking his way across the stones. 'Come my love,' she said, with one white arm stretched out to him. 'I have been thinking of what you told me a year ago and I have had this cauldron filled for you, so that you may bathe in the new air.'

Lleu of the Skilful Hand jumped from his horse. 'But why have you done this?' He asked.

'I wish to frame the scene in my mind, so that I can be sure to keep you safe.'

Lleu was amused by this. 'You are a strange girl.' He took her in his arms and kissed her.

Her tongue was at the corners of his lips and suddenly the lemon taste of ferfain was in his mouth. At this the lust came on him and Blodeuedd felt it, but she unpinned his cloak. 'Wait,' she said. 'First you must wash.' She lifted his mail shirt and stripped down his chequered trews. She drew him to the cauldron and helped him to slide into the heated water.

For an hour Blodeuedd soaped her husband, first his back and wide shoulders, then his chest. Into the cauldron she had cast a tied bunch of camomile and lavender. Lleu closed his eyes and sighed amongst the drowsy fumes that rose from the water.

Blodeuedd then soaped down under the water to his belly and her husband's cock. He groaned with renewed ardour.

'Come now,' said Bloduedd. 'Rise up in the morning breeze.' Lleu stood and the water fell from his tough golden skin. Blodeuedd went to the trees and brought back snow white buck from where it had been tethered. 'Here,' she said this will help you step down.' Gold and freshly washed, with his lust thrusting and risen, Lleu of the Skilful Hand put one foot on the lip of the silver cauldron and the other on the warm white back of the buck goat.

There was a sound of the wind being sheared. Such a sound can only come from secret dark spear. Lleu's back arched and he screamed, for the blade had caught him in the guts, and although the shaft fell away the blade hooked fast because of the barbs. Lleu screamed again and threw out his arms. Now he shrieked and this was terrible for suddenly he rose in his agony and became an eagle, golden and knife-beaked. He flew off into the west and was gone.

From the hill called Bryn Kyvergyr Goronwy the Staunch had cast the spear that he had spent a year in making. He then came down through the trees and taking Lleu's horse he pulled Blodeuedd on behind. They rode back to Mur Castell, where that night Goronwy knew again the secrets of her body. For a week after this Goronwy rode the cantrev with his men, so that everyone would know that he was the new master. Word quickly came across the mountains to Lleu's great uncle, Math Son of Mathonwy, and to his uncle Gwydyon. Like a drought-struck oak Math sat saddened and gloomy in his hall, pondering the news. At last he smoothed down his great auburn beard and sent Gwydyon out to search for their nephew.

All across Gwynnedd and the spread of Powys Gwydyon rode, asking for news of Lleu. Many had heard about the treachery but no one could tell him anything more. So he rode to Arvon. Tired and cold, he found a large hut near the cliffs of Pennardd. It was empty, but the fire was warm, so he went in and lay down, for the night was coming on.

Gwydyon was at the edge of sleep when the farmer came in with three of his men. He was talking as he entered. 'Swineherd,' he said. 'Has that big sow returned from her wandering?'

'She has,' replied the lad. 'As surely she does every evening.'

The men were surprised to find Gwydyon lying at the hearthside. He sat up and they saw his well-cut clothes, and his sword resting by his side. The farmer was about to speak when Gwydyon addressed the young swineherd. 'Where does your sow go?' He asked.

'Well my lord,' he said. 'All I know is that she frets until the sty is opened and then she takes off on her own, away from the other pigs. I have no idea where she ventures.'

'See here,' said Gwydyon. 'I have three golden coins. These are yours if you wake me in the morning and take me to your sow before you open the sty.'

'Gladly my Lord,' replied the swineherd.

At that they all fell asleep by the embers of the hearth.

The swineherd woke Gwydyon and gave him a bowl of cold water. Together they went to the sty. The sow was big and red, with powerful shoulders. She was pushing against the gates and squealing to be let out. 'Stand ready,' said the swineherd. He drew back the gate and the sow bolted up across the hill.

Gwydyon saw that the slopes were no place for a horse, so he took off after on foot. She was fast this big sow and it was hard to keep up with her. Nevertheless, he chased her up a narrow stream into a place of spine ridges and broken rocks. Several times he thought he had lost her but he followed the broken twigs and crushed bracken until at last he came to a wild valley where there had never been any men.

Gwydyon came upon her grunting under a wind-whipped oak tree. He walked quietly towards the sow. He looked down and saw that she was eating gobbets of rotten flesh and wriggling maggots. There was just this one tree in the valley and two small lakes on either side. Gwydyon looked up into the branches and saw an eagle there. It was wounded and quivering this bird. Every time it trembled chunks of putrid meat and worms fell away from its side. Gwydyon beat the sow away with the flat of his sword. Then he sat on a black stone. He thought for a while with his chin resting on the pommel of the sword. Then he closed his eyes and threw back his head to sing an englyn -

'Oak grown old between two lakes,
Dark branches blackening sky and glen.
I will not lie,
These feather flowers are Lleu's.'

The eagle bent its head sideways and looked down at Gwydyon. Then it dropped down to the middle branches. Gwydyon closed his eyes and sang another englyn up through the leaves.

'Oak enduring on a high plain.
Rain does not soak it.
Nine times has it been stricken.
In its branches rests Lleu, Skilful Hand.'

The eagle leaned its head again. Then it dropped down to the lowest branch and stared long at Gwydyon as he sang a third englyn.

'Oak grasping the steep slope
Is the refuge of a noble prince.
If this is true
Lleu come now to my knee.'

The eagle gave a thin cry and with, a whisper quiet as snowfall, it fluttered down to rest on Gwydyon's knee. The bird was limp and damp and its wound stank. Gwydyon struck the eagle with his wand and a tremor convulsed the feathers. He found himself to be holding his nephew in his arms. Lleu was famished and sick. He looked to be as near death as any creature Gwydyon had seen.

He lifted him and carried him down to Pennardd, and then on to Math's fortress at Caer Dathal where they healed him.

In a year Lleu of the Skilful Hand had recovered his strength. His figure had broadened again. His golden skin had toughened like waxed leather. His face was blunt. His eyes had become restless, like those of a long-kennelled hunting dog. He came to Math and Gwydyon when they were confiding in the hall. He entered suddenly and his voice had a low throb to it, like a drum beat at the gates. 'It is time to go and get my vengeance.'

'Aye,' replied Math. 'The day has come.' He turned to Gwydyon. 'Go, call all the host of Gwynnedd to us. We shall ride to Mur Castell that was given by me to our nephew and we shall reckon with Goronwy the Staunch.'

Blodeuedd was in her bed. It was an autumn morning and her eyes had a dark fuchsia hue. She had dined on wild duck and blackberries with Goronwy. Then she had lain alongside him and coaxed him to love her, as she had done every night for the two years since she had plotted against Lleu. Her husband had hardly flickered in her mind for a long time. She thought she remembered that he had become an eagle and had flown towards the mountains.

Goronwy the Staunch sang to her each evening. She adored his brown curls and his soft voice. He did not rise and leave her for weeks. Every sunset he returned to find and Blodeuedd waiting in her gown of petals and seeking his smile. She was made for love and that was all.

But this morning she awoke alone. She gathered the blanket around her shoulders and called for the boy who was her servant. He shuffled at her door, unable to raise his head and look into her violet eyes. 'Where is the Lord Goronwy?' she asked. The boy could not answer. . .

. . . For lashing his horse Goronwy the Staunch was riding hard for his stronghold at Penllynn. A message of warning had come in the night. Goronwy had slipped through the door like a ghost in the darkness. His chequered cloak trailed away behind him. His brown curls were soaked with rain.

In the hawk's cry cold noon, the host of Gwynnedd stood at the walls of Mur Castell where the lovers had trysted. But the gates were ajar and the only life within was an old dog chained in the yard.

Yellow flames sent sparks into the night sky. Lleu and his guards were all around the campfire. The horses were nodding asleep behind them. A tall man came into the circle, without sword or shield or helmet. 'My Lord, Goronwy the Staunch wishes to atone for his great offence. He has sent me to offer gold and land.'

Lleu of the Skilful Hand stood up and went to the man. His voice was like a drum in the darkness. 'You are bold to bring such a message. Your master Goronwy took my wife. He cast a poisoned spear into my guts. I flew as an eagle into a wild valley and green carrion was my only meat. He lay in my bed and my wife was under him each evening. Neither gold nor land will atone for this.'

'Is there any word you wish me to take back to him?' asked the messenger.

Lleu put his blunt face close to the tall man.

'Goronwy will come to the white stones by the river. He will stand naked as I was when he cast his barbed spear. He will stand in the same place as I did and he will wait alone for me to hurl my spear at him. Only this will suffice.'

The cousins and brothers and mailed soldiers of Goronwy stood away from him on the ramparts of Penlynn. He looked out across the low hills. He pushed the dark curls from his eyes. His men looked surly and leaned on their swords. Goronwy turned to them.

'This reply is no good.' He said. 'Is there any among you who will stand in my stead and accept the spear thrust of Lleu?'

A hoarse chorus erupted. 'By our honour, we will not.' The men spat at his feet one by one and told him that, if he would not be the man in this, they would drag him to the river.

'Very well,' said Goronwy. 'Here comes the dawn. I will ride to the white stones.'

So in the pale morning he undressed on the bank. His hips were narrow and his manhood shrunk tight in the cold. In a while he saw a man descending from the hill called Bryn Kyvergyr. Down through the trees he came and Goronwy saw it was Lleu of the Skilful Hand. He halted on the far bank. The water chattered between them. 'See me here,' shouted Lleu. 'I come in full sight of you, instead of hiding, as you did.' He cast off his cloak and whirled his spear around his head. 'See this spear,' he said. 'It has a clean point, where yours was barbed and poisoned.' Goronwy said nothing. He just stood and cupped his crotch.

Lleu spun around and limbered ready to throw, but just as he did Goronwy darted aside to stand behind a white stone. Yet there came a shriek, like an eagle's cry and this was the sound of Lleu's bright fresh spear. And there was Goronwy splayed and arching in agony. For the spear had gone clean through the stone and broken his spine. Pinned and coughing in his blood Goronwy died.

In the scree on the mountainside Blodeuedd knew there was a stone hut, where she would be safe. Her serving boy had told her of it. He had drowned in the torrent of a high stream as he tried to help her across. Slipping from her hand he was washed away. Pale and young this boy; as he went down among the boulders Blodeuedd saw him look her in the face for the first time and the last.

Without pausing she went on, above the trees, up the slopes of broken rocks. In this bare place Blodeuedd shivered for there was nothing green. There was a stung glitter in her violet eyes; a look of numb wonder, that the world had grown hard and jagged around her. She had no idea why Goronwy her lover had abandoned her. She had no idea that he was at this very moment fixed against a white rock by Lleu's spear - the point slicked and greasy with the last pulse of his blood.

The serving boy had told her that the mountain path came to a last bend and once past it she would find the hut made of slate.

Her dress, all stitched from spring flowers hung against her slim curves. Her red hair shone in the keen, high air. She put out a hand to steady herself as the path turned and there was the little hut . . .

And there was Gwydyon waiting for her. Gwydyon, who had helped call her to life under the stars, to be a bride for his golden nephew Lleu.

'Sit Blodeuedd, here, upon this flat stone,' he said. His voice was calm. He looked at her, this girl who was made for loving. The wide blue of the sky was in her sapphire stare.

'I will not kill you,' he said. She smiled at this. But Gwydyon held up his hand. 'No Blodeuedd, there is no mercy here. I will do worse than killing you.'

Though flowers know no pain or anguish and Blodeuedd was conjured from meadowsweet, oak and broom she quailed suddenly at his words.

'For all your disgrace and for the terrible shame you brought to my nephew I will speak this tynged over your head – You will go forever into the form of an owl. You will be forever friendless and outcast. All other birds will fear and hate you. Gliding, white and alone your cries will mourn forever under the cold moon until the last day.'

When Gwydyon had spoken an owl took flight from the flat stone and a litter of petals blew away on the wind. Down, down, down went the owl to the forest below and was lost, but its cries were like tears sewn into the seam of the evening.

Painting the Myth

*T*he roots of the stories which became the myths of Britain and Ireland reach much further than the shores of these islands. Indeed, many of these tales were already old by the time they were first recorded, taken from the mystical oral tradition to which they belong. Whether as modern dispensations of the ancient shamanic traditions, or the Sumerian death and rebirth cycles embedded in Celtic and Roman religions, our myths have been enriched by incoming cultures.

Studying the rich wordplay of Steven O'Brien, I understood early on that the golden poetry and underlying metaphor of the stories would require more than literal representations of the subject matter. I approached this by making hundreds of sketches and copious notes based on my own knowledge and further research into the history and traditions which accompanied the mythology. The result was a complete painting for each story, a blending of fable and symbolism intended to be read as much as viewed, alongside Steven's existing words.

As the interpretation of a story can depend on the way it is told or written, the same is true of the construction of the visual image. In my opinion, painting is a visual language, its origins in the cave art of Paleolithic people convey the deeds of ancient hunters and hero's and the struggles of their everyday lives. These images were probably revered by their descendants in much the same way as the tapestries, illustrations and paintings of our own ancestors have come to be by those of us seeking meaning and a connection to a gloriously depicted past. From the drawings of the ancient hunters, come the genesis of myth, passed down to scribes, druids, monks and illustrators, each with their own agenda for the re-telling of such tales to their audience and the generations that will follow.

Mythology has influenced culture, religion, philosophy and sciences such as psychology, impacting heavily on the work of Freud and more importantly, Carl Jung, who incorporated mythological figures into his series of archetypes. Comparative studies have been conducted by influential writers such as Manly P. Hall and Joseph Campbell, the latter who pioneered the concepts of the hero's journey and the monomyth which are acknowledged by many to be essential reading to those studying the origin and relevance of myth.

For me, the importance of the Britannic Myths lies not just in the human struggle with the darkness of it's own soul as represented by the wraiths and giants of antiquity, but as the journey of the spirit, to attain higher purpose and ultimately, God. I have attempted to show this in the representations I have created for this book by depicting figure, symbol and metaphor within paint. The resulting images hold not answers, but clues as to why the myths of our past are more relevant now than ever.

Joseph Machine, Somerset, 2017

Steven O'Brien is a widely published poet, novelist and editor of *The London Magazine*, and lecturer at the University of Portsmouth, where he leads the MA in Creative Writing. He is also Visiting Fellow of Creative Writing at University College Chichester. For him this all started with The Leprechaun...

Joe Machine is an award winning British artist. Born in Chatham, Kent in 1973 into a deprived environment of crime and vice. Early on, he began to use art as a way out of his surroundings. His immediately recognisable paitings have heard him an international reputation. Focusing on religion and mythology, his work is steeped in symbolism and esoteric knowledge in the same tradition and William Blake and Aubrey Beardsley. His work has been strongly endorsed by renowned UK art critic Edward Lucie-Smith, for whom he has illustrated two books of poetry. He is the painter in residence for the Prometheus Project in Trieste, Italy. He currently lives in Somerset, England, with his wife ad four children.

Further books exploring ancient myths from countries and cultures worldwide, written and illustrated by authors from those cultures are planned, with a further two volumes scheduled for 2018, edited by Steven O'Brien, Joe Machine and Robert Peett.